Gregg Holt

The Secret Burial Grounds of Knocknakil

Published by

LANTERN TOWER

An Imprint of Melrose Press Limited
St Thomas Place, Ely
Cambridgeshire
CB7 4GG, UK
www.melrosebooks.com

FIRST EDITION

Copyright © Gregg Holt 2010

The Author asserts his moral right to
be identified as the author of this work

ISBN 978 1 907040 25 2

Printed and bound in Great Britain by:
The Good News Press, Ongar, Essex

Chapters

Chapter 1

Uncle Jim Reilly

GRAHAM'S HEART STARTED TO POUND AS HE heard the footsteps and the door open. His Uncle Jim had arrived back from seeing to the chickens and would now sit down with his tea and chat. The anticipation started to build, he felt excited as Jim stopped to take a couple of deep puffs on his pipe, filling the immediate air with sweet smelling tobacco. This was the time of the day after the daily farm jobs had been completed that he usually furnished his nephew with his good old Irish tales and stories.

Jim looked at Graham, pointing his pipe in his direction and started, "I tell ye this lad it has been a strange day". Graham leaned forward anxious for his next instalment.

"Those leprechauns are getting mischievous!" he proclaimed.

"I found one in the chicken shed this morning, as real as you sitting there. 'Give me your pot of gold', I shouted!

"The leprechaun looked at me all serious and replied 'Oh well you caught me red handed, you had better pass me that shovel behind you'.

"I looked behind to pick up the shovel but there wasn't one there. I turned back quick to grab him but my small friend had vanished. Only took my eyes off him for a second, but that's all it takes. I tell ye Graham, if you ever manage to catch up with one, never take your eyes off him for a second no matter what he tells you. Once you stop looking at him he will vanish into thin air. I'm ashamed to say it but he gets me every time that leprechaun does. Maybe you might have more success, hey Graham."

He stopped to take a drink of tea and few more puffs on the pipe.

Gregg Holt

Graham's Uncle was a traditional old Irish farmer, well into his seventies but still very active with that fresh healthy look that someone living in the country has. First impressions were deceiving, only the hint of grey catching the light gave some small clues that he had been around for some time. He had a warm glow on his chubby cheeks and a rounded nose which hinted he had a liking for the occasional whiskey. Dark bushy hairs protruded from his nostrils, whilst his ears had become overgrown due to the lack of cultivation.

Jim was not particularly tall; he wore a pine-coloured blazer over his well-worn sweater with its many holes from being ravaged through the years of hard toil. The hard work of farm life had resulted in his huge hands and broad shoulders. When he entered the room, a great presence seemed to accompany him which embossed his authority all around.

Jim put his cup down and continued his tale. "Over the hills last week was a strange man. I had gone down the slope at the rear of the chicken sheds to bring the cows in for milking as usual. The sun was just rising and partially illuminated the sky, creating a dream-like panoramic view. A fresh strong breeze blew against my face, assuring me that this wasn't a dream. As I approached the bottom of the slope, I noticed the cows were agitated and they started kicking out, forcing me to keep my distance.

"It was then I noticed movement on top of the first hill, something was reflecting off the early morning sun. I stopped and focused me old eyes in that direction, then I noticed a tall man positioned on the hill. He was lifting a rock and placing something that seemed to sparkle under it. The stranger must have stood over six feet tall, even at that distance his eyes were striking, blue like the sea surging ashore on a paradise island. Catching the breeze, his ice white robe flapped gently until it came into contact with the grass beneath, concealing his feet. His hair was long and grey with a brilliant single white feather inside a small band. The wind intensified, generating a sudden decrease in temperature that travelled through my bones and eagerly tantalised the back of my neck, leaving the little hairs standing to attention. My body shuddered and shook in shock of the unearthly experience as if I had instantly arrived at Antarctica. My legs felt like lead and started to tremble slightly; if I had wanted to run it would have been futile. A standoff ensued, the man observed me inquisitively whilst I was spellbound gazing in his direction. I noticed out of the side of my vision one of the cows slowly moving around and standing directly behind me, seeking protection from this intruder. Its breathing was heavy, catching the freezing air, resulting in a visible white blast every time it exhaled.

"As the stranger suddenly sprang into life I fell backwards. His robe flapped vigorously behind him as he lifted his staff upwards in our direction. I stepped back and fell onto the cowering Friesian. The cow was having none of it; the great beast jolted me towards this advancing, unidentified mysterious man, probably for his self-preservation. I am not ashamed to tell you I screamed as I started to lose the fight to stay on my feet. My eyes were still focused on the approaching danger as my cry rang out.

"The stranger moved swiftly towards me holding his staff high in the air. Suddenly a bright light from the peak of his stick blinded me for a second.

The cows near me panicked, heading in my direction and leaving me to scramble for cover. The nearest refuge was a large prickly blackthorn bush and I ended up in the middle of it.

When I came to my senses, I looked back in the direction of the strange intruder but he had disappeared, nowhere to be seen. My gaze could have only been broken for a few seconds.

"After this the cows slowly settled and started to make their way up the slope towards the milking sheds. I untangled myself from under the prickly bush and clambered up the hill after the cows. I made my way back to the farmhouse to tell Kathleen all about my encounter."

Graham's Aunt interrupted the story at this point.

"Ah Jim, you will leave the poor lad traumatised and having nightmares!"

"No, it's OK Aunt," Graham insisted and anxiously urged Jim to continue.

Jim pulled on his pipe in deep thought. After what seemed a long time to Graham, Jim sucked on his pipe a couple more times, his tobacco-stained teeth catching the light briefly, and noticing his beloved nephew gazing longingly in his direction he decided to ignore Kathleen's advice.

Leaning forward towards Graham he continued the story. "After milking the cows, curiosity got the better of me and I decided to return to the slope to see what the stranger had been doing around the rock I had seen him move. This time I went slowly towards the place, stopping to check all around me for any signs of the stranger. I moved carefully, scouring the fields and rocky mounds for any signs of the unwanted visitor. It took a few minutes to locate the rock the man had been looking under. All my strength went into lifting that rock; a couple of inches gave way to sunlight and something glittered from the shadow. Using all my strength, I managed to push the rock slightly to the side. My eyes widened as a small round clear crystal rock reflected in the sunlight. I fell to my knees and put my hand out to pick it up. 'What do we have here?' I said.

"Instantly, a burst of movement shot past the palm of my hand and grabbed the crystal. 'Thank you. I think you will find this is for me,' he said snatching at the rock.

"I blinked my eyes a couple of times in disbelief, there in broad daylight was a little leprechaun holding my treasure.

"'This is mine,' he repeated indignantly, lifting the crystal towards the sunlight and examining it closely, his eyes squinting as he visually interrogated the jewel.

"'I think not, I found it!' I shouted.

"'Hmm then we have a problem,' said the leprechaun softly.

"'Did you pick up the other crystal?' the leprechaun continued, pointing at the rock.

"I glanced back at the rock, instantly realising that I had taken my eyes off him. He had vanished yet again; I could not believe I was gullible enough to fall for the same trick a second time."

His Uncle settled back into his chair now slurping on the brew Kathleen had made for him. Calling his nephew by his pet name 'Spud', he suggested the two of them go for a walk alone and get some fresh air. Graham was overjoyed at this idea and sat on the edge of his chair anxiously waiting to start out on their adventure.

Against the wall in the large kitchen stood a hefty range. Kathleen loved baking passionately and excelled with cakes and Irish bread. There was always something baking or cooking on the range, especially when relatives like Graham were visiting. It was a soft yellow in colour which had faded over time, giving it a rustic look. There were scorch marks around the side indicating that danger was never far away. Turf was the fuel used for heating and cooking which was cultivated from the bogs around Mayo. It has a pleasant satisfying aroma which drifts up the chimneys of the farmhouses scattered around the luscious countryside and the unmistakable odour slowly wanders around the green rocky fields.

Each year Graham and his parents holidayed in County Mayo on the Atlantic coast of Ireland. This lasted for two weeks which included daily visits to his Aunt and Uncle on the mysterious farm of Knocknakil. The greeting from his Uncle was always the same, "Welcome Spud", spoken in a soft, deep Irish accent, followed by a firm handshake.

Jim's hands were enormous with skin like sandpaper and every year Graham's knuckles collapsed under the pressure and he ended up falling to his knees begging Jim to have mercy. Graham often wondered why Jim needed his Massey Ferguson tractor when he retained so much strength in his hands.

It was a fine summer's day on Knocknakil; the air was full of harmonious sounds of birds sharing their songs. A short distance along the lane, a large flock of starlings gathered in their hundreds, chattering away. They settled in a large lime tree before suddenly taking back to the air to go through the same sequence all over again.

Jim urged himself out of his chair and beckoned Graham.

"Are you ready then, Spud?"

Before Jim had finished his sentence, his nephew was already on his feet and heading towards the doorway.

They made their way outside as Jim reached for his trusty brown hat which he never left the house without.

"I have been planning to speak you recently Spud, now you're getting older and I won't be around forever." His voice was serious and Graham sensed this was not going to be a casual chat. Jim led the way from the farm, opening a large gate to a field they seldom visited.

"The story I was telling you earlier was all true. There are secret, mysterious and unexplained things on this farm." Jim stopped, turned and looked Graham straight in the face. "Spud, can I trust in you?"

Graham nodded incessantly, a little bewildered.

"Everything we discuss is secret; you cannot tell anybody about our conversation, agreed?"

His nephew was still nodding, not quite sure what to expect. "Agreed?" Jim said again. Graham managed an unsteady "Yes" as Jim's serious voice registered with him.

They walked on a little in silence and when they came to a small hill Jim stopped and sat down on a large rock. "Sit down Spud while I explain. On this farm centuries ago, lived a civilisation of children. They were a peaceful and friendly society, who were quite shy and secretive. As in all walks of life, some people resented them and were afraid of them. An old man known locally as Boggot betrayed this group of people. He was sure they possessed special secret powers and he wanted them. He traded their location to a notorious Viking known as Gregorian, telling him they had many treasures and secrets.

"They attacked and plundered, murdering most of the race of children. He handed over some of the survivors to the Boggot who interrogated and tortured them to find out their secrets. They never cracked. It was rumoured that a great warrior heard of their fate and rescued the survivors. Unfortunately, the Boggot escaped, vowing to track them down one by one. The survivors later returned and buried their families along with their secrets. For safety, the remaining children were separated to live in the four different provinces of Ireland. Even today, you will have heard the legend. To your generation they are known as leprechauns and now you will understand why they are rarely seen."

Graham wasn't sure what to make of this tale; a small grin appeared on his face, expecting his Uncle to start laughing. However, Jim's face was stern with deep frowns appearing, he was very serious. He stood up and started walking on. The conversation fell silent as they passed over gently sloping hills. Graham noticed a stream some way in the distance that they seemed to be heading towards and the silence was broken.

"Spud, you need to be cautious around that stream, it's very dangerous," said Jim, pointing ahead. "Hidden underneath the surface is a swallow hole!"

Graham quickly interrupted. "A swallow hole, what is that?"

"Yes, that's what it is called and it is a mysterious phenomenon. If you stray too close it will suck you down into the stream. I have never known anybody to be seen again if dragged underneath the surface. Nobody is sure why this happens or what it is. All I can tell you is it is very strange. If you think it is just an old tale I can tell you I have lost a couple of my cattle through that hole never to be seen again and if it can swallow cattle there is not much hope for a young boy.

"A couple of years ago a young farmer completely vanished on his way over to Knocknakil. He was a pleasant young man, good footballer they said, not a trace. The only clue they ever found was down by the stream, some handprints that were imprinted on the soft ground. Whoever made those marks was being dragged away into the stream!" Jim turned and started walking again, this time away from the stream.

Graham dropped behind his Uncle as he moved away; he kept stopping to look back at the stream, amazed at what he had just been told. In fact he was so engrossed with the stream he hadn't noticed the lake they had been approaching and which was now just in front of him.

His Uncle stopped, looking out over the surface of the small lake. Graham caught up and gasped. He had been coming to this farm for years but he had never noticed this lake before. It sparkled in the sunlight and large razor sharp reeds around the side stood to attention.

"When the young farmer disappeared the local authorities turned their attention to this lake," Jim told Graham. "They thought he might have fallen in and drowned; rumour has it they tried to drain the lake for forty days. Eventually they gave up, saying it had no bottom. My father always said when he was young there were tales about this lake having no bottom. I feel that one day Graham, you will come to find out more about this place!"

Jim was moving again before his nephew was ready, leaving him to jog to catch up. A short distance later they arrived at a circle of large rocks on a small hill. They stood alone and proud, protruding several feet out of the ground. Moss had been creeping around the smooth surface of the rocks, indicating the site had existed for millennia.

Graham moved into the centre of the circle, calculating what the structure could have been used for all those years ago. Moving closer to one of the stones he noticed strange markings engraved deep into the surface, similar to letters of today's alphabet. There was a letter which resembled an 'e', although it was facing the opposite way, a straight line like 'I', and a 'P' on its side. He presumed it was some type of ancient writing.

Patterns were etched in among some of the letters and were also familiar: diamond shapes all linked together in straight lines, single wave lines crossing over each other which reminded Graham of radio waves he had studied at school.

He was rubbing his hand across one of the rocks when Jim drew his attention to a small cross carved out of rock just beyond the circle. He could just make out behind it a small hole in the ground. There were two large rocks dropping down a few feet and a small archway leading deep into the earth.

Graham moved away from the circle and stepped down into the small archway.

"You are stood in the exit of a secret passageway Spud!" Jim said quietly as he crouched down next to his nephew.

"This passageway is from the old abbeys a couple of miles away. When the Vikings used to raid the abbeys, all the clergy and people escaped to safety here next to the ancient ritual site," he explained, pointing over to the stone structure.

Graham gazed into the tunnel but the darkness did not reveal any secrets.

"This was used on many occasions and is still a secret today. Not many people know about this and it has to remain this way, do you understand?"

Jim asked Graham in a serious voice. Graham nodded, still trying to take it all in.

Jim, defying his age, quickly stood and beckoned his nephew.

"Come on Spud, we should start heading back before the others start sending a search party out for us."

Graham, still trying to gaze down the passage, pleaded for a little longer but Jim was now moving swiftly away. He climbed out from the ground and ran to catch up with his Uncle.

The rest of the walk back was in silence and the sun had started to set. The flocks of starlings were now heading their way and blocked out the sun for a few seconds. Hundreds of them chatting with each other as they flew above. It was just then that one scored a direct hit on Graham, a big white splat right on the top of his head. Everybody thought it was really amusing when he returned to the farmhouse, except Graham who felt very embarrassed. Aunt said: "Don't worry sunshine, they say it's supposed to be lucky."

The following day on his return to Knocknakil, Graham headed off alone over to the hill Jim had been describing in his tales.

As he reached the summit, the air turned cold, nipping at his skin. The hairs on his neck stood to attention and his heartbeat increased. An uneasy feeling settled throughout his body, leaving his legs tingling, sensing the need for flight. His eyes widened, astonished at the vision that had just appeared.

A shadowy transparent image drifted along the valley below. Dressed in battle armour with a large rectangular shield, it moved towards the next hill. The apparition wore a white cloak flowing behind, the sword sat in its belt and his long blonde hair was contained by a tight metal band with a symbol on his forehead. Suddenly he stopped in his tracks and stared menacingly at Graham. After this glance he turned away and walked into the hillside, slowly disappearing below the surface.

After a few seconds Graham gasped, instinct returned and he ran frantically back to the farmhouse. "What's up Spud, you look like you've seen a ghost," Jim said, looking over in Kathleen's direction with a meaningful look. She dropped her head; the secret burial grounds were going to be rediscovered through her nephew and this caused her distress.

It was heading towards the end of Graham's holiday and despite him prompting his Uncle on several occasions there was nothing further said about swallow holes or secret passages. He didn't discuss the warrior apparition or secret passageway with any of the family. Although he found it difficult, he did manage to keep his promise. They left Ireland heading back to England the next day and all he could think about was the secret passageway and Jim's parting comment. "Remember, you made me a promise." It wasn't long before the bumps in the road started to fade and Graham fell soundly asleep.

Six months later, just after Christmas, Graham's Mother and Father informed him they were going to Ireland again for their summer holidays. He was ecstatic, in an instant he started to remember about the secret passageway and warnings about staying away from the dangerous stream. The experience had faded and the mysteries of Knocknakil had been forgotten until now! It all came flooding back and he kept thinking about his Uncle Jim and finding out more about the farm and its hidden secrets.

One dark winter's night in February, Graham had gone to bed as normal but for some reason he could not settle. He felt restless, something was not quite right but he didn't know why. Graham heard his parents go to bed and pretended to be asleep when they came in to check on him. Sleep still eluded him and he climbed out of bed to gaze out the window. It was dark in the rear garden and there was a slight breeze which was moving the branches on the large sycamore tree. He started to imagine shapes within the branches as they swayed from side to side. Suddenly a vivid image startled him; Graham saw a cloaked figure move by the tree. He instantly jumped back into bed deep under the covers, certain a mysterious apparition was on the prowl. Eventually he convinced himself that the darkness was playing tricks and fell asleep. Within minutes, Graham was dreaming about a screaming noise outside in the back garden, after a few seconds he woke startled, he wasn't imagining. This noise was haunting, with very high penetrating pitches in waves like a siren. Never in his entire life had he heard anything so inexplicable.

Graham tried to build the confidence to look out the window. He placed his foot on the floor when the unearthly screech broke the silence again. Graham gasped and threw himself back into his bed. Now wide awake, it happened again, about three more times. Each time his heart pounded and he lifted the covers right under his chin. Graham was waiting in anticipation for it to start again but it was the phone that rang next, which made him jump. A deep sense of anxiety grew, not quite knowing what to expect. His Mum ran out of bed and answered the phone. She did not come back upstairs and after a few minutes he decided to go and check what was happening. Slowly he crept downstairs and couldn't hear much at first. But just as he passed the creaking stair he heard his Mum was crying. "What's up Mum?" he said, sensitively entering the room.

"Oh Graham," and she started to cry even more. She beckoned him over and she gave him a big reassuring cuddle. "It's Uncle Jim Reilly; he passed away peacefully in his sleep last night."

Graham was stunned and fell backwards onto the floor; he burst into tears, saying "No, no this can't be right!"

Chapter 2

Boggot Hole Clough

AGAINST THE DARK SKY, A FLASH OF a cloak swished in the wind as an ominous image landed next to the back door. The dark countryside lit for a few seconds as a door briefly opened and slammed shut. The new arrival entered the forlorn dilapidated cottage situated deep in a large steep valley. A low mist draped the steep sides of the rock-strewn valley, making it almost impenetrable. There were no traces of civilisation to be found in this remote mountain range somewhere on the West Coast of Ireland. The cottage was in a bad state of repair; the windows were boarded up and the roof had collapsed some time in the past. The only living beings that passed over the summit of the valley were the occasional sheep who gazed longingly at the luscious untouched grass below. The suppressive atmosphere and fear for their own safety prevented them from progressing further despite the temptation of fresh pasture. A farmer occasionally passed by but was oblivious of the existence of this long-forgotten structure and didn't so much as look in the valley.

The interior was sparse, with broken rocks littering the ground. In the corner of the cottage were stairs leading deep into the ground. The glow from a fire dancing around could be seen emanating from the bottom of the stairs. The image slowly glided down the stairs towards the flickering light. It wore an old monk's cloak and no face could be seen inside the dark hood.

The silence was broken as a deep serrated voice spoke quietly. "Sucillian, my faithful servant, I need your help."

The hooded being nodded his head in acknowledgement.

12

In the room a large fire crackled and burned violently, throwing haunting shapes around the damp walls covered in green slime. On a spit above the fire the skin of a pig bubbled and squealed as it slowly cooked.

Sucillian looked beyond the fire where the voice had come from deep into the corner of the room where the light failed to penetrate. He could see the occasional glint of dark eyes when the fire shot burning shrapnel in that direction.

"The time is fast approaching when we will learn the location of the long-lost secrets buried away somewhere deep in Mayo. The two young children will soon learn where the secret entrance is. Keep following them Sucillian, don't harm them until they have delivered us our secret!" He grinned slightly, revealing his razor-sharp teeth for a brief second.

His dark eyes were flickering in the fire light; there was no blinking just a rigid stare. They were cold and sinister, staring right through Sucillian which would have unhinged the strongest of men.

The hooded being was undeterred and nodded slightly, accepting the orders.

"There is something else." The ground started to shake, with parts of the remaining roof collapsing in a hail of dust. Above the valley a deep dark cloud gathered pace, building up just above the ground. The black cloud rolled quickly along the ground as if a great storm was building. Flashes of lightning were cracking out in all directions, sending loud rumblings echoing and shaking the valley floor. Rocks started tumbling downwards, crashing through the long ferns and heather. The cloud proceeded hastily towards the cottage, spreading wider and higher, developing into a vicious weather front. The door on the cottage violently flew open as a hurricane-strength wind whistled through the enclosed space, shaking the entire foundations of the cottage. Sucillian was almost knocked off his feet as his cloak slapped and flapped under the pressure. Small shrubs and dust spiralled around the room, having been uprooted by the strength of the wind. The thick cloud surrounded the cottage, being drawn in through the small doorway. Within seconds, the oppressive weather front had completely forced its way inside, leaving the valley to recover from the severe battering from the flash storm.

The door slammed closed and immediately calm returned; the fire could be seen and heard again. Sucillian turned as the sound of heavy footsteps entered the room. Large figures passed by him towards the dark eyes in the corner of the cottage.

Towering above this hooded fiend stood several large scary-looking men. They were covered in large animal furs which stretched around the torso, each with a broach holding it in place just below the chin. Chain mail draped down their bodies, reaching their thighs. In their left hands were large round shields with sharp steel points in the centre aiming outwards to inflict the maximum damage on any enemies. On their heads were helmets of various designs: a couple had two horns pointing out of either side; others had nose plates and one had eye protectors, signifying these men were Viking warriors. They had belts around their waist with exaggerated buckles, which held long swords and short razor-sharp daggers.

The voice from the corner of the room broke the silence whilst still remaining hidden in the shadows.

"Sucillian, these men are notorious; they are brave vindictive soldiers who fought with me for centuries. They, like me, want the hidden burial grounds and will stop at nothing to find them, anybody who gets in their way…" 'Crash' – a large sword landed in the middle of the room, shaking violently.

One of the Vikings stood forward and retracted the sword into his belt. He spoke with the hidden being still remaining in the shadows. They spoke in an ancient dialect, undecipherable to anybody unfortunate enough to hear their conversation.

"Gregorian, go take your men and wait in the decaying forest until my ambassador summons you!" said the rough voice, with his eyes hauntingly penetrating out of the darkness.

Suddenly, the Vikings turned in synchrony and moved up the steps towards the door. The wind increased and the door burst open with hurricane strength as the dark cloud rushed into the room. The soldiers were swallowed by the mist which quickly digested them and withdrew back through the valley and up the steep slopes. Just past the valley, it quickly dropped towards the ocean. Low mist reduced visibility; any outsider would just see the fog. The dark blur joined the low-lying mist over the crashing waves. Just protruding through the obscure air, a wooden carved shape revealed itself. It was the face of a monster at the bow of this primeval vessel used by Vikings centuries ago. The mist evaporated out to sea and with it the crew and sinister boat had gone, leaving no indication of what had just happened.

From the other side of the valley a dark figure approached. His movement was much more deliberate and controlled, slowly bounding down the sheer slopes. He had several battle scars etched into his face. A long knee-length dark coat flapped behind as he moved swiftly towards the cottage. A tall man, with hair as dark as coal which was knotted and shoulder length, pushed open the cottage door. There were heavy footsteps as he approached the stairs and proceeded down into the darkness. Passing by Sucillian, he towered above him. Not even noticing he was there, he entered the murky shadows of the strange beasts' realm.

"Ahh, my ambassador Iroquois, the time has come to repay your debt," said the serrated voice from the gloom.

"It's about time, do you know how long I have waited to be free of your shackles," replied the visitor, his voice scornful and treacherous.

"Honour your word, find me the burial grounds and you are a free man. There is a young boy who has recently arrived in the county; I feel he holds the key to the location. Sucillian here knows where you can find the boy and will accompany you." A finger from the gloomy shadows pointed at Sucillian and the visitor turned towards the hooded being. Sucillian nodded in acknowledgement of his instructions.

"What about the boy?"

"I want the burial grounds; the boy is of no significance. Do what you have to!"

The dark-haired visitor looked at Sucillian and let out an excited untrustworthy laugh which echoed around the cottage and the surrounding valley. Sheep in the surrounding fields dispersed quickly, sensing danger was near.

"In the decaying forest await some of my soldiers; they will follow your every order. Don't let me down!" he ordered, still remaining unseen in the gloom.

Iroquois did not reply, he shook his head and groaned disgruntled at having to accept orders. He moved towards the fire where the pig was slowly cooking. Grabbing one of its legs, he ripped it away from the body and instantly bit into it.

Turning round, he looked at Sucillian with flesh hanging from mouth. He stared for a few seconds and then returned and tucked into his feast.

Chapter 3

Knocknakil

RAHAM WAS DEVASTATED BY THE SHOCKING NEWS that had arrived from Ireland. This only worsened when he realised that his Mother was going over for the funeral without him. Graham tried frantically to advocate a place for himself but his parents insisted his schooling was more important. His Father had work commitments and couldn't travel; but also insisted it was not the best place for a young lad. Graham detested his Dad for this decision but only managed two days of not talking to him.

Deep down, Graham struggled to accept there was not going to be any more secret conversations or walks with Jim around Knocknakil. This left him feeling cheated and resentful towards his Uncle for not finishing what he started.

Fortunately, this faded over the next few days to be replaced by happier memories although he still felt some disappointment that his mysterious adventures were over.

Graham's holiday was quickly approaching but he showed no excitement or desire to returning to Mayo Abbey. His parents were worried as usually he was climbing the walls with excitement counting down the hours. His Mother had an idea and disappeared for a couple of hours before returning.

"Graham I have a surprise for you," his Mum said, grinning broadly.

"What is it Mum?" he replied, not even bothering to lift his head.

"Lorna is coming with us to Ireland."

Graham jumped up off the chair, cracking his head on the shelf above. At that point he didn't know if to laugh or cry; this was great news coupled with a searing pain. Luckily the pain didn't stay too long and the excitement came flooding back like a large emotional wave the size of a tsunami. Realising he was not being cool, showing emotion, Graham changed his tune, "Well if she has to I suppose it's OK".

Lorna had been one of Graham's best friends since they were knee-high to a grasshopper, as Uncle Jim used to say. Although it wasn't cool to hang around with a girl, she was more like a boy than some of his other friends and they always had great adventures together. Graham recalled the time they went fishing at a pond in some local fields. They set off down a country lane past some really expensive houses. It was at one of these houses that a large guard dog lived. Deliberately it hovered at the large front gate waiting to ambush any unsuspecting visitors. Every time they went past it barked and snarled at them trying to break out through the gate, which fortunately was very high with little chance of the dog escaping. It was an Alsatian which was practically all black with some brown patches along its stomach. It was an extremely angry animal, intent on escape to inflict damage on anybody unfortunate enough to cross its path. This day they went past and as usual the dog was snarling and frothing at the mouth, doing his utmost to escape. Lorna decided to have some fun and started showing the dog her bum saying "I bet you would like to chew on this wouldn't you". This made the dog even more furious and it barked fiercely as it made several attempts to jump over the gate at them. They made a few jokes and decided to carry on to the pond. It wasn't a particularly successful day's fishing and after a couple of hours they decided to head home.

Passing by the houses again they were deep in conversation when their thoughts instantly switched, with the sound of a dog barking in the distance. They both looked across the road towards the notorious house with the irate Alsatian. To their horror, they realised the gate had been left open and instantly recognised that there was no barrier between them and the dog they had been tormenting earlier that day. Immediately, the dog noticed the familiar tormentors and with great speed set off toward them to pursue his prey. They both froze, glued to the spot; not that running would have helped as this animal was running at the speed of sound. As it started to get within a matter of feet, they could see its brilliant white teeth, especially the fangs. Their hearts started to beat faster and they braced themselves for the sharp pain of the razor sharp fangs penetrating their soft skin.

The rabid beast started across the road and sprang through the air launching his calculated final attack.

Simultaneously, a car appeared from nowhere at great speed and braked heavily, making a terrifically large screech followed by an enormous yelp, leaving the air with a strong smell of burning rubber!

It hit the dog and sent it sprawling right across the road. It took a few seconds to take all this in. Lorna pulled at Graham shouting "Quickly let's go!" and they ran off as fast as their legs could carry them. It took them several months before they built up the courage to go past the house again but they never saw the dog as they passed.

Just at that point there was a knock on the door, it was Lorna. She came running in and Graham noticed she was just as excited about their holiday together as he was. Lorna had never been to Ireland and Graham quickly started to tell her stories about Mayo Abbey and the mysterious farm of Knocknakil. Lorna listened intently, which made a change, she was hanging off Graham's every word. The two enthusiastically exchanged thoughts and ideas to create the perfect framework for a fantastic holiday. Lorna was the same age as him, thirteen; her skin was slightly darker with long dark hair, which was shoulder length. Even though she was the same age she had started to develop curves and bumps which Graham found a little uncomfortable, particularly as the clothes she had started to wear were quite tight. She was pretty, with brown eyes and a slim figure and he was always surprised about her appetite for adventures. Every time she smiled, the cutest dimples appeared in her cheeks which deep down Graham found were her most characteristic quality. They were good friends and didn't argue too much, although Graham did find her to be stubborn, a little like himself. She was very single-minded and adventur- ous; fortunately they shared the same tastes and inquisitive nature. The rest of the night was spent sparring ideas and discussing what adventures they had planned. These were centred on Knocknakil and helping around the farm.

Graham mentioned the dangers passed onto to him by his late Uncle about the stream and Lorna's face lit up "This I must see," she replied eagerly. Lastly, Graham mentioned the ghostly figures walking through hillsides which left Lorna looking at Graham a little sceptically.

The pair were interrupted. "Lorna it's time to go home. Her Mum had called to pick her up and they reluctantly wandered down stairs. Nevertheless, the scene was set and the excitement returned in abundance.

The day eventually arrived. Graham opened the door to Lorna and helped her load her bag in the already packed car and they had an uneventful drive to Holyhead to catch the ferry. Lorna had never been on a boat before and was very excited. Once on the boat, she seemed to lose her enthusiasm and by the time they reached Ireland she was rather pale. His parents, Graham and Lorna made their way across Ireland to the West Coast, the excitement building as they got closer to their destination. When you're approaching Mayo Abbey, the roads start to bend and dip which reminded them of fairground rides with that funny sensation in their tummies. Graham's anticipation levels started to rise to new heights and he found himself staring out the window thinking about his late Uncle. Approaching the familiar places, an unexpected strong emotional feeling embraced Graham without warning as he reminisced. Lorna looked across and noticed a small tear trickling down the side of his defined cheek bones and pointed chin before eventually disappearing below his t-shirt. Graham liked to wear casual sports wear, particularly tracksuits and jogging bottoms. Lorna was quite attracted to the sporty look which well-matched Graham's long athletic build and brown straight hair. He had light freckles on his face and arms which became more prominent in the sun.

A short while later the car pulled up outside an attractive little white cottage with stone patterns on the front. A modern property, it had a well-stocked front garden with a small concrete path dissecting the eye-catching array of flowers and bushes. Slowly drifting up from the chimney, a thin wisp of pale smoke carried the delicious scent of smouldering turf in the direction of the newcomers.

"We're here Lorna, this is it!" Graham announced, scrambling impatiently out of the car.

From the front of the house they had fantastic views of the West Coast of Ireland, Croagh Patrick, the largest mountain in the whole of Ireland, and the unpredictable Atlantic Ocean. As they climbed out of the car, Graham noticed something out of the corner of his eye.

An outline of a figure standing across in a field, wearing what appeared to resemble an old monk's cloak with a hood pulled right over his head. The image lifted its head in Graham's direction. Graham paused, staring directly at him; he could not distinguish any facial features beneath the hood and started to think back to the previous February, the frightful night when he had heard the strange cries and caught a glimpse of a strange image outside. Feeling apprehensive, he turned and called to Lorna.

"Have you seen that man over there?" he said, pointing in the general direction he had been looking.

Lorna quickly glanced round and shrugged her shoulders.

When Graham turned back he had gone. He found this astonishing as he had only turned away for what could only have been a few seconds, yet the image was nowhere to be seen.

Graham was slightly unnerved. Although his best friend and family were close by, he actually felt quite isolated.

The house they were staying in was miles from the nearest village; in fact the closest neighbour was about two hundred yards away, which conveniently was the local shop and pub. The only other structures nearby were an old abbey, a church and graveyards. At night there was no light, it was pitch dark everywhere. The local pub left a light on at night and the occasional car or tractor would also light the surrounding countryside as it passed through.

They quickly ran into the house and Dan treated Graham to his customary greeting, a chin pie. Lorna watched bemused as Dan rubbed his chin on Graham, his stubbly growth irritating his immature skin. It was always fun for the first few seconds which generated Graham's infectious laugh, followed quickly by a fight to escape his clutches seconds later. Lorna was lucky; Dan only reserved this tradition for his nephew. Dan was in his early sixties and was very fit. Although he had grey stringy hair, you just wouldn't believe his age. He was very hard working and was proud of the house he had built a few years ago. This was the very house in which they were staying. After their brief hello to Dan, Graham showed Lorna the house and their bedrooms for the next two weeks. They were at the rear of the house with views over a small field; just beyond the end of the field was an old church and cemetery. There were two small bedrooms, with a joining door, which had a slight musty smell to which they quickly became accustomed. Lorna quickly claimed the nearest room for herself. They started to unpack their cases and put clothes in the wardrobes and drawers. By this time it was starting to get late and the sun was starting to set. The delicious smell of cooking started to touch their senses and caught their attention. They made their way quickly to the living room for a spot of supper followed by tea and Irish Mikado marshmallow biscuits, just what was required after a long day's travelling. The open fireplace hosted a welcoming fire that was well under way and gave the cottage an unmistakable homely feel to it. They sat on the couch watching the flames dance and listening to the snaps and cracks of the burning turf. It wasn't long before they started to lose the fight to stay awake. There were no arguments from them when Graham's Mum suggested they turn in for the day. With freshly brushed teeth, they went in the bedroom and proceeded to close the curtains. As Graham started to pull the curtains together he noticed to his horror the strange man from earlier, right outside the window. He was inches away, looking straight at him, but still he couldn't see his face. At first Graham couldn't speak but eventually he managed a startled scream as he fell backwards away from the window, Dan came running in quickly.

"What's the matter?" he said with a broad Irish accent.

"Th… there is someone out there!" he replied breathlessly. Dan quickly ran out, and Lorna could see the light from the torch dancing around the shadows as he was having a good look round. "No one there!" he said as he returned to the bedroom shivering, "but it's ice cold out there." After a few minutes Graham started to settle down wondering whether his eyes were playing tricks on him. Although he was quite shocked, he did start to nod off and fortunately had a good night's sleep.

The next morning, Graham woke to the sound of a tractor and peered cautiously out of the bedroom window. In the field just beyond the house a large tractor was busy moving up and down the meadow.

Walking into the living room, Dan was crouched stoking the fire.

"Morning Graham, did you sleep well?"

"Not too bad, thanks."

"Have you recovered from the shock last night?"

"I think so," Graham replied, remembering the apparition with a shudder. Dan sat back up into his chair.

"There have been some strange things happening around here over the past few weeks. A few of the local farmers have noticed what they thought was an old monk wondering around the fields. My Grandfather used to tell me a story about a faceless monk.

"He said there was no face because he possessed no soul; the cloak he wore was stolen from a monk who was never seen again.

"It is rumoured he is searching for secret burial grounds somewhere in Ireland. My Grandfather used to say he would never stop searching until he found the sacred site. There is a belief that sometimes when a relative or someone close to you passes away a haunting scream can be heard that echoes three times. If you hear this scream bad news will soon be arriving at your door step. Grandfather used to say this was because the angels had arrived to escort the departed of good people when the evil spirits were present."

Graham started thinking about his own experience earlier in the year.

"Dan, can I ask you a question, it might sound daft?"

"Course you can Graham."

"I think I heard the cries of the monk on the night when Jim died, what would that mean?"

"Hmmm," sighed Dan loudly.

"Did Jim ever tell you any old tales about Knocknakil?"

"No, never," responded Graham quickly, not knowing where to look. Dan looked at him suspiciously. "All I can say is that these are old tales and if you think you heard the screams on that night, then who am I to argue. One thing is for sure that, Jim was a good man. That monk must have thought he knew something about the sacred burial site."

At that point Lorna walked in, stretching her arms right up into the air as if finishing a race in first place. Graham couldn't help but notice her top riding up revealing her belly button.

"Where are my manners," said Dan, "who wants a cup of tea?" and hastily he went off into the kitchen.

Graham sat back in his chair, thinking about the conversation with Dan.

After a satisfying full cooked breakfast they headed out to explore the surrounding area. The weather was cloudy but not cold or raining which was overall good news although the mountains were hidden in low clouds. They wandered down the lane to the local shop to explore and spend some of their holiday money on sweets. Considering the remote positioning of the shop in the country, there were quite a few customers inside. One farmer was speaking to the man behind the counter, telling him that his cattle were all very restless last night. "Something was scaring them, one of my prize heifers had tried to run through the dry stone wall, so it must have been something quite scary, they're never bothered by foxes or any other type animal. It's a bit of a mystery," he said as he picked up his supplies and left the shop, acknowledging the two youngsters with a smile. They walked into the shop and wandered around the untidily stacked shelves, looking for some interesting items. The couple paid for their sweets and left the shop, moving in the direction of the graveyard and discussing the story they had just overheard.

They passed the old church which looked neglected and uncared for. They stopped at the entrance to the cemetery, examining the surroundings.

Lorna sat up on the stone wall, choosing the flattest rock for comfort.

"I'll wait here Graham," she said as Graham opened the old rusty gate and headed in. Lorna opened a packet of her sweets and settled down, sensing this was a private affair.

Graham entered through the old gate and slowly followed the directions he had been given by Dan until he arrived at a headstone with Jim's name engraved on it.

After saying a few words, he started to look around. Just behind was the old church and all around you could see mounds on the ground, which were very uneven although in straight lines. These were the ruins of some of the old abbeys. It was a peaceful and tranquil place and Graham found himself listening to the birds singing and cattle braying in the distance.

His thoughts were interrupted as Lorna shouted "Have you seen him over there?" as she jumped off the wall and nodded her head in the direction of the man she had seen.

Graham quickly turned to look; there was a lane with a large hill in the distance but he could not see anybody.

"Do they have a monastery around here?" Lorna asked inquisitively.

"No, why?" Graham replied, still looking in the direction Lorna had pointed.

"Well that man on the hill had a monk's cloak on, came right over his face," Lorna explained.

The hairs on the back of Graham's neck started to stand up.

"Look over there Graham," Lorna shouted, pointing towards the back of the graveyard.

Graham spun round; the hooded man was there, inside the cemetery and moving quickly in his direction. Graham turned towards him slowly edging backwards. The faceless image was dark and menacing.

"Maybe we should come back later, eh Graham?" Lorna suggested, moving back towards the cemetery gate. Leaving Graham, she quickly started to run.

Graham, sensing the danger, turned and quickly started to run after Lorna. He noticed she was already outside the wall and heading away from the cemetery. Graham glanced back and felt his running was making little progress.

"Quick Graham!" Lorna shouted, panic etched in her voice.

Chapter 4

The Stream

As GRAHAM FRANTICALLY RUSHED TOWARDS THE GAP in the wall, he could feel hot volcanic breath burning into the back of his neck. His lungs were at full capacity and he started to struggle to maintain his momentum. After what seemed like an eternity, Graham scrambled through the purpose-built entrance to the cemetery, landing in Lorna's arms. They both fell backwards, narrowly missing a couple about to enter the graveyard.

"Watch out!" a voice shouted as they continued through the gateway muttering, "Kids of today."

"You alright Graham?" Lorna asked as they both scrambled to their feet.

"Yeah I think so," he replied, quickly gaining the confidence to look back. "Where is it?"

"Don't know," replied Lorna searching the horizon. "It just disappeared." All they could see was the couple Graham had nearly run into standing at one of the graves.

They made their way quickly back to the cottage while they kept checking behind them, hearts beating hard and hands shaking.

Later that day, Graham and Lorna had recovered from their experience and went with Graham's parents over to see his Aunt at the mysterious farm of Knocknakil. Quickly, Graham jumped out of the car and ran into the waiting arms of his Aunt. Squeezing tightly, she held her nephew firmly in her hands; you could only just notice him under her large frame.

"Ah this must be Lorna, you didn't tell me she was this pretty Graham, Welcome to Knocknakil, make yourself at home!" she exclaimed quickly, extended her welcoming hug.

Lorna was lost in Aunt's pleasantly plump figure, being hauled into her soft motherly breasts. Instantly she warmed to Kathleen, identifying with her kind-hearted manner. Although Lorna did have an Aunt somewhere in America, Kathleen was the type of relative she always imagined her to be. However, she did sense a head teacher element to her personality which she soon put to the back of her mind as she didn't intend to cross her.

"Come in, I have the kettle on for ye," she said, heading into the farmhouse.

The pair of them followed warily, chuckling about the bear hug they had just received.

They followed her in to the main room for tea and some delightful homemade cakes.

"Hmmm, these cakes are delicious!" Lorna said to Graham, speaking with her mouth full and crumbs escaping freely.

"Why don't you take Lorna for a tour of the farm Graham?" Aunt suggested, offering Lorna another cake.

"Yes, cool," Lorna nodded, grabbing a cake sharply.

Having finished their cakes, they were quickly onto their feet and heading outside for Lorna's first tour of the farm. As Graham opened the door, heavy rain fell into the house leaving their plans in tatters.

Returning into the house, Aunt was midway through explaining strange happenings on the farm to Graham's parents. Lorna noticed Kathleen's short manageable brown hair and creases starting to appear around her mouth with a slight bow of flesh under her chin. As she continued her story, she sat a little un-ladylike, her elasticated skirt riding slightly above her pop socks and slippers.

However, taking all this into account, Lorna was really taken with her warm facial features and affectionate persona.

"The cattle and sheep are acting strangely; they won't go past the first hill in the direction of the stream. Even the weather has been bad, dark clouds blocking out most of the sunlight. Some of the local farmers are complaining about strange creatures stalking their land making strange noises at night. All I know for sure is I heard it myself and not long after the cattle became very restless and came to the gate trying to come back off the fields into the milking sheds.

"A few weeks ago very early in the morning, just after sunrise, I set off towards the hills and stream to bring the cattle in for milking. Over on top of the hill I saw a man dressed in what I thought was an old white coat; he had a long staff and white hair. He didn't belong in this era that's for sure, and was quite elderly as if he was a chief elder from some sort of ancient tribe. He looked over in my direction and I froze. I was captivated for what seemed like ages. Eventually he smiled and casually walked off in the direction of the stream. As he disappeared over the other side of the hill, the cattle started making there way over towards the sheds. Although I was frightened I didn't feel in any danger and I haven't seen him since".

The rain was still falling heavily and they reluctantly accepted defeat and arranged with Kathleen to visit the following day. Graham's parents were going visiting some friends in Galway and thought it might be a little boring for the children.

Pulling out of the farm into the dark night, Graham's Father lit the countryside with the full beam of their car.

The darkness consumes the countryside at this time of night and spooky shadows crept towards the car trying to devour its occupants. The lights manage to fend off the ensuing attack as they drove down the deserted lanes.

As the car lit up the dark road, the moths flying around become attracted to the lights and made their last fateful flight into oblivion. The children gazed out of the window, confidently feeling the car's speed offered them protection from the unfamiliar terrain and its occupants. The dips and bends slowly faded as they pulled up outside the little attractive cottage and the safety of home.

After an uneventful night's sleep, Graham and Lorna made their way over to Knocknakil to spend the day on the farm. The door to the house was open but Kathleen was nowhere to be seen.

"You don't think something has happened to her do you?" Lorna inquired.

"Hope not," Graham replied, starting to think about the events she had described the day before.

"I thought I heard voices," Kathleen said, exiting the milking shed behind them.

They both jumped and looked at each other, with smiles slowly replacing the shocked expressions.

"Come on then you two, I have a job for you both." And she turned and walked towards the pig sties. They followed quickly behind and noticed two large buckets next to the entrance of the sty. Each bucket was full to the top with scraps and swill, an enjoyable feast for any pig. Graham cleverly allowed Lorna to enter first, the mud inside reached over the halfway point on their Wellington boots. This made walking quite difficult and each step needed caution and control.

After a few seconds, the sow noticed the arrival of her breakfast. She hurriedly moved towards Lorna, who was now a little apprehensive and noticed Graham hovering around the gate. The sow was hungry and was nudging the bucket with her soggy snout trying to empty the contents. The mud squelched as she aggressively bumped into Lorna who started to realise the enormity of this simple task. Graham and his Aunt were now in fits of laughter as Lorna battled to retain her balance. Another strong nudge at the back of Lorna's knee tipped the balance and she fell into the deep mud. She managed to stop her whole body falling in but her arm was in past the elbow. The bucket dropped and the sow's snout was deep inside, grunting away as she ate.

Graham used the opportunity to casually walk in and empty his contents into the feed tray without an incident. Like a true knight in shining armour, he pulled Lorna by her free arm and into the upright position with a wry smile.

Slowly Lorna squelched her way out of the sty with one of her arms caked in mud.

"Phew, you'll need a good wash now!" Graham chuckled. Lorna was not amused.

Graham was chuckling as they returned to the farmhouse for Lorna to wash off the undesirable and by now stinking muck.

"When you have finished in there will you collect the eggs from the chicken sheds for me and then you're free for the rest of the day?" Aunt called as she walked off into the kitchen without waiting for a reply.

Soon after Lorna had washed her arm, Graham led the way out and towards the sheds where the chickens were kept.

They walked through the large rusted gate at the rear of the farmhouse which led to the main part of the farm including the hen sheds which were still locked with their occupants inside.

The door creaked as Graham pushed it open and the chickens stampeded out, narrowly missing his face in a desperate bid for freedom, much to Lorna's amusement. Feathers floated and the chickens squawked as they bobbed away into the field.

"Grab one of those baskets Lorna," Graham suggested, slowly moving into the shed.

"Phew that stinks!" shouted Lorna, entering just behind Graham and being met by an invisible field of pungent odour.

"Yeah it does," replied Graham in a funny voice, holding his nostrils tightly together with his fingers.

After a few seconds their eyes adjusted to the dark shed, littered with the droppings of countless chickens and the little nests with eggs patiently waiting for collection.

One of the chickens returned clucking loudly, trying to warn off the invaders and protect the eggs.

Graham shouted, "AARGH!" and the chicken fled, leaving a large feather floating in the air.

They collected about sixteen eggs and were just starting back when Lorna said: "I have a good idea. Why don't we draw a picture of Mr. Gallagher, our head teacher, at the back of the shed?"

"What do we want to do that for?" Graham replied, looking at Lorna quite puzzled.

"So we can throw a couple of eggs at him, Aunt won't miss them all!" she said.

"Great idea," replied Graham as a mischievous grin filled his face and they quickly scouted the surrounding area for a stone.

CRACK!! The egg smashed right on Mr. Gallagher's head.

"Great shot Graham!" shouted Lorna and she proceeded to have her shot and also scored a direct hit.

They returned to the farmhouse with eight eggs, congratulating each other on their fine shooting.

"What have you two been up to, you look very pleased with yourselves?" Aunt inquired as she collected the egg baskets.

"It wasn't us," said Lorna looking as guilty as could be.

"What weren't you!" she said a little pushily.

"Throwing the eggs."

Graham stared at Lorna in disbelief.

Kathleen's face turned to thunder; suddenly Lorna recognised the head teacher streak escalating with fury.

"GRAHAM FOLLOW ME!" she demanded, leading the way through the rustic farm gate.

"Chicken OK for dinner?"

They arrived at the chicken shed and the chickens were quite happily walking around pecking at things on the ground.

"What about this one?" she said, pointing at an innocent brown chicken with a little floppy red crown.

Graham, who was not sure what he was agreeing to, nodded cautiously. Instantly Kathleen grabbed the chicken, put her hand around its neck and twisted it violently.

He heard the crunch and instantly realised he had signed its death warrant by agreeing to have chicken for tea.

Graham was horrified; his stomach turned and his face lost its entire natural colour. Kathleen, noticing the impact, walked off holding the chicken by the neck saying "It still requires plucking and cooking yet, I don't suppose you would be much help!".

Graham returned to the farmhouse and Lorna stared at him.

"Oh Graham, you don't look so good!"

"Neither would you if you had been there and watched your Aunt kill a chicken for our tea!"

"No way!" shouted Lorna. "I am not eating it, no way!" she protested.

Kathleen hearing this, shouted "Out with you, go and play!"

They quickly exited the house just in case she changed her mind or gave them some meaningless chores.

Proceeding to the back of the farmhouse, they went through the large rustic gate and past the chickens' shed. The chickens stayed well away from them this time, not that they had the nerve to go anywhere near them after Kathleen's shocking misdemeanour.

Leisurely walking over the hill, they could now see right across the fields at the rear of the farm. Graham's colour started to filter back to his cheeks but the vivid image was still imprinted deep in his thoughts.

Without realising, they proceeded in the direction of the stream.

Passing over a large mound Lorna noticed the rock formations that were imbedded deep into the hill. They definitely looked as if they were man-made although they had deteriorated over time, leaving a suggestion that the mounds had served some purpose in the past.

Graham then became conscious that the cattle and sheep were accumulated around them and none could be seen beyond that point towards the stream.

They continued on, climbing over the hill. As they did so, the atmosphere changed, the air became heavier and their breathing was more laboured. They continued down the other side and onto a second hill, the atmosphere relented and their breathing returned to normal.

A flash of movement to the left and they both looked over, catching something just disappearing out of sight.

"What was that?" Graham asked a little bemused.

Lorna looked at him for a few seconds, deciding whether to answer honestly.

"If I didn't know any better I would have said it was leprechaun. You're the expert on Ireland, you tell me what it was?"

Graham, feeling a little relieved and confused, replied: "Yeah, that's what I thought it was."

They just looked at each other,

"You always said that if you find one, you can demand its gold!" Lorna inquired, her dimples appearing as an excited smile grew.

"Yes, that's right," Graham replied.

Lorna quickly came to her senses. "Come on, then let's catch it!" and she started to run in the direction it had disappeared without waiting for an answer. Graham quickly followed down the second hill, dodging the large rocks.

They were utterly amazed as they peered around the other side of the hill. There, a short distance ahead, was a small ginger-haired man standing about one foot tall. He was wearing a light green tunic that blended into the background extremely well; only the red hair and movement surrendered his location to the inquisitive children who were now intently observing him.

Silently, Graham and Lorna watched the man happily looking around the field.

Without warning, he suddenly looked up, sensing he was being watched, turned around and noticed them looking at him; the three of them were just staring. The man squinted his eyes, trying to get a better look at the intruders. He then turned away, only to look back abruptly after a few seconds. Three times he did this, as if astounded at what he was seeing.

Without warning, he turned sharply and accelerated away, quickly disappearing around another hill. Lorna and Graham responded, striving forward like hounds hunting the fox although it was a little cumbersome running with Wellington boots on.

"What do we have to do when we catch him Graham?" Lorna gasped breathlessly.

"I'm not really sure; just don't take your eyes off him, Jim used to say."

As they arrived around the hill they noticed the stream providing a natural barrier the full width of the farm.

The pocket-sized man was scampering at full throttle towards the stream. Gradually, his pace started to slow and the youngsters noticed he seemed to be tiring. After a few seconds he stopped, bending forward, placing his hands on his hips and breathing heavily.

"We've got him trapped now Graham," Lorna whispered, her hands pointing out the fact the stream had cut off his escape.

Quickly, the mysterious little man looked up with a scornful look upon his face. They started walking cautiously towards him.

With a little jump he turned again and started running towards the stream. Instantly, Graham and Lorna were in hot pursuit as their strides increased impressively. Rapidly they started to gain on him but not in time to stop him reaching the water. The wee fellow dropped down the bank of the stream and out of their sight.

Within seconds the hunters were on the bank searching frantically. Lorna was pulling the reeds apart. "He could not have gone far!"

They searched behind large tufts of grass and even lifted rocks but still there was no sign of him.

"Where could he be?" Lorna continued, her hands held skywards in a confused manner.

Graham just looked at her, shrugging his shoulders in a defeated manner.

Lorna continued "He was here a second ago!" as she moved up and down the bank probing everywhere, even under the rocks.

Lorna then looked around at the stream and said: "Do you think he went in there?"

Graham instantly remembered the warnings Jim had given him about this little deceptive stretch of water. Lorna started to move right to the edge of the water "Be careful!" he cried, "Jim always warned me about this stream!"

"Yeah, yeah, I am not letting him get away even if he's hiding in the stream," Lorna replied defiantly, her finger wagging.

Just under the surface of the water Lorna noticed a large rock. She tried to place her foot onto it so she could look under the water. It was just out of reach. "Come here Graham, let me hold your arm so I can reach the rock!" she ordered, indicating with her hand to approach.

Reluctantly, Graham moved towards her and held out his hand. Lorna grabbed it and they locked hands together as her foot moved away from the safety of the bank.

Cautiously, Lorna placed her foot on the rock checking if it could support her weight fully. After a couple of taps she became confident it would and placed her foot fully on it.

Suddenly the rock fell and violent bubbles rose from below the surface with loud sucking noises. Graham attempted to lean back and pull his friend to safety.

Lorna would not budge, in fact her weight was transferring closer to where the rock had once stood and the bubbles were rising.

"It's pulling me in Graham, HELP," Lorna screamed, panicking.

"I'm trying," shouted Graham, still trying to pull back to the bank.

Time stood still for a few seconds as they appeared suspended in mid air.

Gradually gravity took control of the situation and Graham edged closer to Lorna past the point of no return. They gasped as their bodies impacted into the cold treacherous water; it pinched at their skin leaving them breathing erratically.

Furiously, air bubbles exploded all around, a violent current from underneath menacingly pulled at them. Graham and Lorna wrestled frantically but the pull of the water was too strong and they slipped deep into the darkness.

Chapter 5

Decaying Forest

THE HEAVY FOG LINGERED AROUND THIS FORGOTTEN part of the Atlantic coast. It was strewn with jagged rocks which no sailing vessel dared to navigate. Hidden from view in these treacherous waters was a small island which time had forgotten. The small coastline had large sheer cliff faces and several small bays with shingle beaches. One of the bays, which had deep swirling water, was hidden from sight. The bay's entrance looked well protected by rocks which gave the impression from a distance of a continuous large rock face. However, if you approached from a certain direction an entrance could be seen large enough for an ocean going craft to navigate and enter.

The bay harboured a long forgotten vessel which sat rocking with the wave's motion, offering it protection from the elements and prying eyes. Fifty-foot long, it had one extremely large mast in the middle of the craft and a haunting monster carved into the bow. Engineered entirely of wood, the side of the vessel curved in the centre so it was only a few feet from the ocean level at its nucleus. Several large oars stood to attention, giving the impression they had not seen action for years. The wooden benches which stretched the width of the craft were deserted, only the Ravens sat high on the mast brought any life to this lifeless bay.

Waves crashed onto the pebbled beach trying to reclaim as much of the island as possible. A few feet beyond the shore and shingle stood a large dense and ancient forest; it appeared lifeless and dark. Some of the trees had died and branches fell limp off the trunks giving the impression the forest was dying.

All around the floor lay broken branches. In patches, thick heather blocked any natural sunlight penetrating deep into the centre of the woodland. The forest was eerie in its silence with no birdsong to bring life to the dark and silent atmosphere.

Watching out over the bay from the edge of the shingle stood an ancient-looking man. He wore long cloth clothing with thick animal fur wrapped tightly around his torso. It was held together by a thick gold brooch which sat proudly upon his heavy chain mail. Around his waist a broad leather strap housed a long razor-sharp sword. He lifted off his heavy steel helmet to reveal dishevelled long blonde hair for a few seconds, placing it back carefully so the nose plate sat across the bridge of his nose. His elongated face was overgrown with stubble and a large crooked nose provided evidence of being broken during battle, possibly several times. Swallowing deeply, he drove deep into his chest and spat out a disgusting mix of phlegm which landed a few inches away from his knee-length leather boots. Turning abruptly towards the trees, he edged into the fringes of the forest. After a few large strides, smoke started to drift in the direction he was walking. He continued in the same direction, bending down to pick up wood as he progressed. The undergrowth became thicker the further he ventured into the forest, making him pause for a few seconds to find his bearings. A short distance later the structure of the forest changed, the heather disappeared and so did the trees, slowly but surely old stumps appeared where the trees had been felled and the smoke became thicker. Edging out of the woodland, a large clearing could be seen with several round wooden huts. Smoke bellowed from the roofs and the breeze carried it deep into the trees. Moving towards the nearest hut, suddenly a low growl penetrated the cold air. The man turned instantly towards the noise and there snarling its teeth stood a large wolf. Running to attack him, the beast's fangs protruded from its drooling mouth, excited by the prospect of the attack. Twang, a rope snapped and the wolf howled in pain as it was suddenly stopped in its tracks. The restraint prevented him achieving his target. The wood collector dropped his wood and drew his sword, lifting it aggressively above his head; he prepared to slay the wolf.

"Stop, Guthrum!" came an order from next to the nearest wooden hut. The wolf flinched and retreated slightly, still showing its fangs in defiance.

"Argh, one day you won't be here to protect these beasts Gregorian," he replied, holding the sword aloft.

"Retract your sword now!" Gregorian ordered, placing his hand on his own sword.

Guthrum grunted but retracted his sword; he bent down and collected his wood. The wolf howled loudly as if to celebrate his victory; he was quickly joined by several other wolves filling the air with their haunting and chilling cries.

Gregorian returned into the hut where a fire held pride of place in the centre of the room.

"Do you have trouble Gregorian?" a low profound voice from the gloom asked.

From behind the fire stepped a large monstrous man, battle scars evident across his face. Dark hair which hadn't seen water in years.

"I... I... Iroquois you should have told me you were coming. I would have had a banquet ready," Gregorian replied cautiously.

"Never mind that, are your men ready?"

"Yes of course they are, they are professional soldiers."

"Hmm," Iroquois replied as he slowly circled Gregorian, making him feel very uncomfortable. "There are two children and no doubt that interfering leprechaun will show his face in time."

"Two children and a leprechaun, you want me and my men to fight children!" Gregorian exploded, storming towards Iroquois.

"Silent!" he replied, staring menacingly at Gregorian who quickly remembered his place.

"Sorry sire, that was unforgivable of me." And he bowed his head.

"No doubt that old druid will make things difficult for you, the time has come."

"I will ready the men immediately."

"No not immediately, there is always time to eat." Iroquois noticed a jug and he drank from it, red wine ran down the side of his face and he let out a satisfied burp.

"Gregorian, more wine if you please," Iroquois barked as his hand wiped the remaining drips from his face.

A short time later Gregorian returned with roast hog caught earlier that day in the forest. Several of his men brought potatoes, bread and several jugs of red wine. The smell of the sweetly cooked meat filled the air, tantalising their taste buds and enticing Iroquois instantly to the table. They placed them on a long ancient table with two benches on both sides and they all sat around. Iroquois drooled as he grabbed flesh from the freshly-cooked beast and ripped at it primitively. With his left hand he grabbed a potato and forced it into his mouth, quickly swilling it down with more exotic wine.

The smell drifted far beyond the wooden hut, enticing more interested parties to the dinner table. Peering over his shoulder, Guthrum noticed a wolf's nose slowly edging through the doorway. He hurled the half empty wine jug at the unsuspecting creature, sending it howling out of the hut. Seconds later more howls penetrated the cold breeze as the wolves approached the enticing aroma.

Gregorian's men drank countless jugs of wine as they sang songs whilst jostling with each other.

Iroquois ordered Gregorian out of the hut with him.

"The Boggot informed me it is time. First thing in the morning, ready your men."

"Of course Iroquois, what do you want me to do?" Gregorian replied, nodding slightly.

"Sail to Devil's Point and stay there and await my orders."

"It's a treacherous stretch of water, Devil's Point, Iroquois."

"Not to a captain of your experience Gregorian; it's ideal, you won't be bothered with any unwanted visitors."

A wolf inched towards Iroquois as he slowly drew his sword. Gregorian placed his hand on Iroquois and he replaced it.

"Wolves – vile creatures." Iroquois scorned.

Gregorian whistled deeply and the wolf instantly back peddled obeying his master.

"You have to know how to treat them," Gregorian replied.

"Devil's Point tomorrow!" Iroquois ordered and he walked away into the dark, haunting decaying forest.

Chapter 6

Swallow Hole

EEPER INTO THE DARKNESS THEY SANK, THE water playing with their bodies, forcefully throwing and pushing them, leaving the two very disorientated. Their skin started to numb from the cold as they sank further into the unknown. Graham's hand slipped from Lorna's as they drifted apart and their chests strained under the lack of air and the water pressure. The urge to breathe was incredible and slowly the water forced its way into their mouths. Roving freely, their arms and legs started to go limp, allowing the current to dictate direction, and the darkness took on a new meaning as they drifted into unconsciousness.

Some time later, Graham slowly started to hear a long exaggerated whistle blowing in his ears. A soft tickling sensation followed as water trickled from his ear drum.

"I am not sure your friend is too good," said an unfamiliar distant voice.

Graham presumed he was dreaming until somebody started banging on his chest.

"Wake up, wake up, you lazy sod!" it shouted.

Anxiously, Graham instantly opened his eyes realising he was still alive. There directly in front of him was the blurred image of the little man he had been pursuing.

They were eye level with each other, although Graham was half sat and half slumped backwards. He started to come to his senses and noticed his green tunic was quilted with a belt splitting the middle, supporting a small cloth bag and short sheath with a sword. Dark tight trousers were tucked neatly into what appeared to be fabric ankle-length boots.

Not noticing that Graham was awake he turned and banged on his chest again.

"I'm awake!" shouted Graham, pushing him away and sitting up. The little man squinted at Graham with his twinkly eyes housed in mature eye sockets. The red stubble protruding all around his jaw line started to move as he said, "About time!"

"Give me your gold," he suddenly shouted at Graham, prodding Graham on the cheek.

"What gold?" Graham exclaimed, rubbing his eyes in shock.

"Don't you start," said the little man, "I suppose you're going to say what your friend said, that you were chasing me for mine."

"Well yes," he replied hesitantly, looking bemused and noticing that Lorna was safe and sat up on a rock.

At this the man became annoyed saying, "Everybody knows that leprechauns don't have the gold, it's the humans that have it," and he stomped off in a temper.

Graham sat up. Looking around, he noticed the damp walls of an underground cave around him. A few feet in front of him, a small river surged through the cavern, the water crashing against the rocks and filling the air with tiny droplets of moisture. There was a small pool with bubbling water separated by large rocks next to a shingle beach just underneath Graham's feet.

"You OK, Graham?" Lorna asked, jumping off a small ledge where sunlight was penetrating into the cave and providing some light to the dark surroundings.

"Yeah, I think so," he replied, grabbing Lorna's hand and clambering to his feet.

The sound of the river echoed all around and Graham noticed that it eventually dipped below the rocks and out of sight.

"How do we get out of here?" Lorna asked, her eyes looking all around.

"Don't know, how did we end up in here?" Graham replied, noticing the ginger-haired fellow sat on a rock, his head in his hands.

"Oi, you, how do we get out of here?" Graham shouted across to the stranger.

The question fell on deaf ears as he sat there still shaking his head muttering to himself.

"Come on Lorna, let's try up there where the light is coming in."

Climbing onto the ledge, a small passageway revealed itself as the light shone directly towards them. They pulled themselves up and started to walk down the rocky honeycombed corridor, stumbling occasionally on loose rocks. The light increased and they noticed the cave entrance a short distance ahead. A quiet rushing noise amplified into a howl as they approached, eventually becoming a gale as fresh sea air blew into their faces recklessly.

Lorna climbed up over the rocks partly blocking the entrance, turning to assist Graham.

Standing side by side they gazed out in awe over the frothy crystal blue water of the Atlantic Ocean.

The ocean fought furiously with the ragged rocks on which they stood, thunderous waves crashed, intent on destruction, throwing showers of salty spray over them.

"Look, no way back to land!" Graham shouted pointing behind the entrance to the cave which had now revealed itself as a solitary, isolated large rock.

They both looked back noticing the main land was several hundred feet behind them. Large rocks protruding from the ocean floor were under the same fearsome attack from the white crested waves. It would be impossible for them to attempt to enter the water.

Mesmerised, they gazed at the waves crashing a short distance below, spraying them at every opportunity.

"We better see if we can find some other way back," Graham shouted, pulling at Lorna's arm.

"Come on Lorna!" Graham shouted again, becoming impatient.

"Yeah, yeah, I'm coming, chill out," Lorna replied, reluctantly trying to pull herself away, astounded by the beauty of such a stimulating view which somehow left her feeling liberated.

They clambered back down into the tunnel and Lorna stumbled, landing on top of Graham, their bodies horizontal and staring into each others' eyes, much to his dissatisfaction.

"What is this place?" Lorna inquired quickly, realising the embarrassing position they were in and climbing promptly to her feet. "Do you think that dwarf really is a leprechaun?"

"I think so," Graham replied.

"Well we didn't follow Jim's advice very well did we, eh?" Lorna said, slightly raising her voice and pointing at Graham.

"What are you talking about Lorna?"

"Jim said, don't take your eyes off him, not even for a second; remember?"

"Oh yes," said Graham as he realised the implications. "I bet he's long gone by now. Or maybe he's still there. If so, let's hope he's some use and can get us out of here, considering he has no gold," Graham replied and their pace quickly increased.

After a few steps Lorna suddenly threw her arm across Graham's chest, stopping him promptly in his tracks.

"What's that Graham?" she whispered, her face had drained leaving it colourless.

"Please tell me that I am not seeing a ghostly soldier walking across the passageway?"

"S... S... Sorry Lorna, I can't."

"So are you seeing what I'm looking at?"

"Yes," he stuttered, with his body shaking.

The warrior was radiating against the dark passage. He glanced across, looking right through them, and vanished through the solid stone wall.

They quickly returned to the cave where they had last seen the little man, their hearts beating like drums. Struggling to comprehend what they had just seen, they stopped and fell silent; he was still sat there muttering to himself in a grumpy mood.

"Do you know how we can get out of here?" Graham asked in a quiet apologetic voice, moving towards the leprechaun and noticing he had a trimmed beard and emerald green eyes. Fairly good looking chap, Graham thought to himself.

The petite man looked up at the bedraggled pale pair and said: "There is only one person who will know what to do. Yes, I must take you to see Carragah; he is the wise one and will certainly know what to do!" as he briskly jumped to his feet.

"My name is Graham and this is Lorna," he said holding out his hand in a bid of friendship.

The leprechaun stopped in his tracks and paused for several seconds, looking at them before responding.

"My name is Kiltmagh Brihanny."

"That's a funny name!" grinned Lorna nervously, still feeling the effects from the apparition and not allowing him to finish his sentence.

"I am one of the few remaining leprechauns," he continued.

"Well there is no way I will remember that name," Lorna said, interrupting for a second time.

"I think I will call you Lepy."

The leprechaun shook his head in dismay and started walking. He carried on ignoring the questions Graham and Lorna were now asking as they started off at pace deep into another honeycombed passageway.

Graham and Lorna quickly ran after Lepy to keep close, still apprehensive after the disturbing experience a short while ago. The natural light in the cave quickly faded away, leaving them in virtual darkness.

The leprechaun pulled something out of his cloth bag and a light started to shine from his hand. It looked like a small glass ball. Considering its size it was emitting a powerful bright light. The cave came alive with eerie shadows dancing all around.

Slowly they travelled through a dark tunnel which had been carved through the solid limestone. Lepy's light shone several feet ahead fighting with the darkness intent on keeping its passage secret. Underfoot were square cobbles revealing some purpose to the existence of this passageway. Their eyes started to adjust with the aid of Lepy's light and Graham noticed some markings on the walls.

"Hey Lorna, these markings on the wall, they're the same as the rocks at Knocknakil," Graham said, stopping and running his fingers through one of the marks.

"I wonder what they mean?" Lorna asked, slightly tilting her head to the side to improve her view.

"It's ancient writing from a Celtic tribe entrusted to protect part of this land thousands of years ago," the leprechaun said, stopping and returning to look at the markings with them.

"What does it say?" Lorna asked, still moving her head from side to side.

"Now that, I don't know," replied Lepy. "Before my time I'm afraid. Carragah might be able to help, come on we must carry on." And he turned, walking off leaving Graham and Lorna in darkness.

They quickly followed, not wanting to be left in this dark dungeon, and as they caught up they noticed several pillars carved into the rock.

Glancing from side to side, Lepy started to look behind each one as they passed.

"What is it Lepy?" Graham asked, quickly sensing the small leprechaun was on edge.

"We are being watched."

"Who by?" asked Lorna.

"I don't know but I sense danger is close by," Lepy snapped back.

They carried on past the pillars, further into the darkness and the unknown.

"Hey look, fireflies," Lorna exclaimed, pointing back towards the pillars.

They looked back and noticed red dots appearing from behind the pillars.

"They're not fireflies, they're Shrakes!" Lepy exclaimed, and Lorna and Graham now realised the red glow they were observing indicated danger!

Out of the darkness they could now distinguish the shape behind the scary eyes. Cat-like figures, their fur coats more ragged, with tufts of hairs scruffily sticking up. Their back two legs were larger than the front two, giving a slight resemblance of rabbit's hind legs. When they moved, they bounded with the extra strength provided by these powerful limbs. Slowly they crept up towards the party. Lorna noticed piercing blood red eyes and two sharp fangs protruding dangerously from their slavering jaws. Their ears were slightly pointed, resembling those of a cat, but these beasts were no cats. Graham's heart started to pound vigorously, realising that they were in immediate danger. His adrenalin started to pump around his body, reaching each and every muscle, ready for the trouble ahead.

"So Lepy, I don't suppose these are vegetarians are they?" Graham whispered, gazing at the sharp protruding luminous fangs.

"No, we need to get to Carragah pronto, RUN!" Lepy screamed.

Quickly turning, they started running at full capacity further into the abyss. Hurriedly glancing back, Graham noticed the red eyes and fangs dancing in the darkness as they started to catch up with them.

Lepy's light started to reveal a large steel-arched door covering the entire passageway and, more importantly, blocking their escape!

"We're trapped!" screamed Lorna, panic etched in her voice.

Graham dropped slightly behind and a growl penetrated the air a few inches behind.

Suddenly the door started to open and creak loudly as it moved. Graham felt a gust of wind just behind his neck as a sharp claw narrowly swiped by. He was running as fast as his quivering legs would carry him but the growls were gaining inch by inch. Graham noticed the door several feet away just as Lepy disappeared behind it. He started to lose hope and prepared himself for the inevitable attack from behind, expecting the fangs to penetrate his skin any second. Against his better judgment, he glanced backwards as one of the Shrakes jumped in the air with its fangs and claws ready to slice his skin. It was too late to escape and Graham prepared himself for the worst. A second Shrake joined in and the two collided in mid air as they attempted to shred Graham's skin.

"Quick Graham!" Lorna shouted.

Graham responded and drove forward as another slice caught his shirt. He was running faster than his body could manage and gravity dragged him down as he fell hard to the floor.

Lepy appeared and held up his light. The Shrakes were dazzled for a second, which gave Lorna the opportunity to pull Graham behind the door and to safety.

The leprechaun joined them in a flash and there was a large shudder, the sound of heavy metal reassuringly sealing them in.

Graham collapsed on the floor, his heart visibly pounding through his chest, not knowing whether to laugh or cry.

The room they had entered was extremely tall and perfectly round with four arched doors at three, six, nine and twelve o'clock. The roof was dome-shaped, increasing in height in the middle. Around the wall were little fires, old type torches burning. Graham climbed to his feet and patted himself down. "We'll be safe in here," Lepy said and he sat down on a chair with a round table situated in the middle of this circular room. On the table there was a three-pronged candle stick, with what looked like a hundred years of cobwebs on it.

"What is this place Lepy?" Graham asked, looking inquisitively around the room, trying to forget what had just happened, although his shaking hands and dry throat were constantly reminding him.

"It's where the old tribes from Mayo Abbey used to meet with Carragah generations ago," he replied.

"Who is Carragah?"

"He was Lord over an ancient civilisation that was entrusted to protect this land," said Lepy.

"Protect this land? Carragah?" Graham repeated.

"Don't you ask a lot questions. Next you will want to know what colour underwear I've got on!" Lepy said. He jumped off the chair and started to stomp around the room, going round in circles which Lorna found quite amusing, trying her best not to laugh.

Graham decided not to ask any more questions. Silence fell in the room as Lorna started to regain control of her desire to laugh at the newly-acquired stroppy friend.

At that point Lorna noticed a slight vibration on the floor, it started to increase slowly. The vibration became stronger and proceeded up the walls. It gathered momentum, the room now started to shake vigorously and the table moved from side to side. The occupants started to lose balance and they put their hands on the floor to prevent themselves from falling.

"What's happening?" Graham shouted, but the other two were to busy battling to remain upright to respond. Out of the corner of his eye he noticed the door at twelve o'clock slowly starting to open. The ground instantly stopped vibrating and a very slow creak could be heard as the door opened.

Graham and Lorna stared over in nervous anticipation at the dark doorway. After what seemed like an eternity, a strange figure started to appear...

Chapter 7

Carragah

DARKNESS SLOWLY GAVE UP ITS SECRET AS a tall man walked into the room. He had grey hair and wore a white robe with a gold rope tied around the waist. His long face had high cheek bones and a pointed nose; his blue eyes appeared heavy yet rich with wisdom. Carrying a large staff, he glided across the floor. The robe had gold embroidery around the arms and neck line resembling the diamond markings on the rocks near the bottomless lake.

Graham instantly remembered the description of the man his Uncle had portrayed the previous year. Uncontrollable thoughts quickly escalated and Graham envisaged this man navigating the long ages of the earth. Yes he was old but somehow he had avoided the ravages of time. Contours on his face told many stories yet his physique resembled a much younger man.

Their apprehension grew, not knowing what to expect, so they slowly edged away from the newcomer.

In a soft voice he spoke. "Don't be afraid, I will not harm thee."

Moving further into the room he approached Graham who in turn gradually backed away.

"He looks like a Druid," Lorna whispered.

"Carragah, I did not know where else to go," Lepy said, edging cautiously towards him.

"Kiltmagh my faithful friend, it's good to see you again after all this time."

"They stumbled across the swallow hole."

The druid man lifted his palm, preventing Lepy from completing his sentence.

"Fear not Kiltmagh, I am sure we can resolve this situation," he said, continuing to move towards Graham.

Lorna looked at Graham, tapping her finger against her forehead and pointing at the newcomer, suggesting instability.

"I wouldn't expect you to understand Lorna," the mysterious man said.

"How do you know my name?" Lorna quickly demanded, looking around the room confused.

"I am Carragah, last survivor of an ancient civilisation entrusted to protect these lands hundreds of years ago," he replied, raising his staff slightly, at which point they all noticed a small, slightly glowing glass ball inset into the carvings.

"Looks like it too," Lorna interrupted, then quickly threw her hand over her mouth, realising these were words and not thoughts.

"Lorna, quiet!" Graham shouted, looking sternly across. Lorna raised her hands suggesting she didn't know how it happened.

Carragah was enchanting, mystifying and Graham felt safe in his company. He wanted to know more about the recent mysterious events. Considering Lepy had brought them here it was reasonable to expect he could offer some explanation.

"There are a lot of strange things occurring at the moment, do you know anything about them?" Graham cautiously asked.

"Well Graham, I am not quite sure where to begin," he replied softly.

"You can start with that ghost we've just seen," Lorna interrupted.

"Hmmm," Carragah replied, his long fingers rubbing against his chin.

"A warrior ghost I presume?"

They both nodded, looking at each other. Carragah walked away, continuing to touch his jaw and look down at the floor.

"Through the universe there are strong energy streams. On each planet there is a point where this invisible energy naturally accrues, known as Springs. It disperses from this point throughout the planet down certain energy lines, providing the natural resources to promote and support life. All life on Earth depends on this energy without realising its importance.

"For thousands of years people have managed to break into the energy lines and in fact some cultures depended on them. There have been some who, for their own reasons, have tried to use this energy for their own devious ends. On planet Earth there are four Springs dispersed around the globe. Two are located under the oceans and one is hidden deep beneath solid ice. The only spring on land is here in Ireland—"

"It's Knocknakil, isn't it?" Graham interrupted.

"Yes, that's right Graham," Carragah said, pausing for several seconds before sitting at the round table.

"In this room over the centuries the head tribesman appointed to protect each Spring would meet, hence four chairs each set at the points of the compass," said Carragah, pointing at the four chairs around the table.

"Today's society has forgotten the natural energy resources provided by its host and is engrossed in artificial technology. Unfortunately, there are some who for thousands of years have been searching this land in the hope of locating the Spring."

"What happens if they locate this place?" Lorna interrupted.

"Well we can't deny that you don't speak your mind Lorna," Carragah replied, smiling. Lorna looked a little embarrassed as they all stared at her.

"Now then, if somebody managed to locate the Spring and access the energy supply, realistically they would have limitless power... which could... well be used for any purposes. There are some evil lords endlessly searching for this place and you cannot mention this discussion to anybody!" Carragah snapped, rising to his feet.

"What about the man in the monk's cloak?" Lorna exclaimed, realising she was interrupting yet again.

"In a monk's cloak you say?" Carragah said, looking alarmed.

"Yes, and you can't see his face!" she promptly replied.

"They are close to the secret burial grounds," he mumbled, rubbing his chin, his eyes straining, deliberating his next move.

"Centuries ago, we became friendly with the monks from the old abbeys who extended a hand of peace. Whilst in the abbey it was attacked by Vikings. They killed many of the monks and stole their treasures. The monks hid us in a secret passage until the raid was over. Thirteen monks had been murdered and hundreds of special artefacts were stolen or broken. The monks were peaceful people, astonishingly brave, placing our safety before their own. After the raid they allowed us back into the abbey and included us with their educational studies and prayers. Scholars from all over Europe and beyond came here to Mayo to study. We learnt how the Vikings had been visiting this part of Ireland pillaging and stealing for years.

"However, there was one Viking tribe they feared more than any other. This group was led by a large fearsome commander called Gregorian. He was not searching for gold or treasure, and showed no mercy to anybody unfortunate to cross his path.

"After all the assistance the monks had shown, we agreed to assist them in their struggle against the Vikings.

"Using some of the tall round towers situated along the coast, we were able to gain early warning of inevitable attacks. We had prepared over the months since their last raid creating this network of underground tunnels.

"Some time in the ninth century the dreaded Vikings returned, in dozens of large ships with haunting engravings carved into the bow of each vessel. Hundreds of bloodthirsty soldiers intent on murder and destruction were jeering as they approached the coast.

"From the cave systems we were able to redirect some of the Earth's natural energy. We used this with devastating effect; before a ship had even reached the shore we had destroyed it along with its occupants. Regrettably, one of the ships escaped, which was the most feared of all, Gregorian's.

"These are no ordinary disorganised band of Vikings, looking to steal and cause mayhem. There is something different... they are disciplined and ruthless.

"I believe they represent a dark and sinister order, educated in the way of the universe searching for the Earth's natural spring. Imagine Gregorian controlling the Earth's natural power for evil purposes. It would probably mean the end to civilised life on Earth and possibly the Universe. Over the centuries, evil people just like Gregorian have known about the existence of the springs. Only the commitment of a few good people has guarded and protected this secret. The most effective defence is to keep its location secret, which has worked for hundreds of years." He moved forward on the chair, leaning on his wooden stick.

"Following the destruction of the Vikings, rumours spread throughout the lands of Ireland and beyond. The local people scoured the coast searching for treasures washed ashore from the broken wreckage. Other more sinister-minded people arrived from darker lands, concealing themselves in the background, probing for any clues as to what happened to such a strong army. Fortunately, as time passed it was generally accepted that the ocean had claimed the ships in an intense storm.

"My people decided to stay here below the plains of Mayo to avoid any unwanted attention being drawn towards this place.

"I feel that you two youngsters have a large part to play in the protection of the secret burial grounds."

Carragah paused, looking skywards. "I sense a presence I haven't felt for centuries, dark clouds are gathering out in the Atlantic." Carragah urged himself to his feet with the aid of his staff. "The last time I felt like this was when Gregorian escaped our clutches.

"Oh, I am an old man babbling on; we should be getting you young children home."

Turning to look at Lepy, Carragah said: "Kiltmagh, I appoint you to protect and guide these two."

"What me, I'm a mere Leprechaun, no match for Shrakes and dark evil forces."

"Kiltmagh, your size does not reflect your courage and bravery; you will serve them well."

Lepy started to cough. "But Carragah, I'm too old for this job. A couple of centuries ago maybe but not now," he said, as he bent his arm, feeling the biceps muscle on his right arm.

"Sch... Kiltmagh you are also chosen to help and protect this secret, now go take them home and return tomorrow!"

"Kiltmagh, we call him Lepy, it's easier to remember," Lorna piped up.

"Lepy... that actually works," Carragah replied, smiling and nodding his head.

At this, Carragah stood and left the room. The door at six o'clock opened and Lepy in a disgruntled voice said "Follow me" and left the room muttering under his breath.

Graham and Lorna anxiously glanced around, hoping the beasts from earlier were not going to reappear. Reaching the shelved area, they instantly remembered the tribulations after falling into the stream.

Lepy looked at them confidently and said "Hold my hand and you will be fine".

They both glanced at each other but remained static. Lepy stared into their eyes and said "Trust me".

He held out both his hands and they slowly moved towards him.

Chapter 8

Iroquois

EPY LED THEM AWAY FROM THE SHELVED area and slightly upstream. He turned to the cave wall and Lorna noticed stepping stones protruding out of the stone wall leading to the roof of the cave. Like a shot, Lepy climbed up the steps and disappeared into a small hole and out of sight. Seconds later his face appeared, "What are you waiting for?"

Lorna beat Graham to the first step and quickly disappeared. Graham quickly glanced round, aware he was on his own, and he quickly ascended the stone blocks. As he reached the top, he noticed a small ledge with sunlight shining on it. It was just wide enough to crawl through. Like a commando, Graham moved through the ledge until he saw Lepy and Lorna stood up in the open field.

"Now you know where the secret entrance is, it saves getting wet," giggled Lepy.

"Ah, I know where we are," Graham said, looking around. "There's the stream."

"Graham, Lorna." It was Aunt's voice shouting in the distance. They looked back towards the farm and Aunt came over the hill. "Where have you two been, did you not hear me shouting?"

Aunt trundled off with her Wellington boots, making gestures towards the farmhouse. Lorna turned around. "Will we see you soon Lepy?"

"Where has he gone?" Graham gasped, noticing he was nowhere to be seen.

Aunt interrupted abruptly. "Come on you two, no dawdling, your tea's on the table and I have waited long enough!"

They followed Aunt back up towards the farmhouse, struggling to keep pace with this energetic elderly lady. Sure enough tea was on the table; Graham sat down and pulled in his chair ready to tuck in.

Suddenly his mind returned to earlier in the day when his Aunt had encouraged him to pick a chicken for tea. Graham's stomach churned as he noticed the cooked bird and realised the implications of his actions earlier. Lorna grabbed a leg and ripped it off, biting into the juicy meat oblivious to the moral dilemma Graham was suffering. Graham, feeling guilty and slightly nauseous, nibbled at a couple of potatoes, much to his Aunt's disapproval.

Graham's parents returned to collect them.

"What have you two been up to today?" asked Graham's Father, pulling up to the table and tearing off some chicken.

They looked at each other and started laughing.

"What's so funny?" he enquired, still chewing on the chicken.

"Nothing, we had a great day. Can we come back tomorrow?"

"Well if it is OK with Aunt?" and the three of them gazed over awaiting her response.

"Of course you can. No funny business though!"

"Funny business, what have you two been up to?" his Father enquired, a slight frown appearing across his forehead.

"Oh nothing," they replied, quickly leaving the table together.

Returning to Mayo Abbey, the summer sun had started its descent behind the ocean. It was a picturesque sight, watching it edge slowly past the crooked slopes of Crough Patrick and out of sight. An affectionate pink glow warmed the western sky, Graham and Lorna watched as it turned darker.

"Red sky at night, shepherd's delight," Graham said gleefully.

"What does that mean?" Lorna replied, mesmerised by the sight.

"It means it is going to be a nice day tomorrow, it's an old wives' tale I think." They both returned into the cottage, with Lorna reciting the new verse quietly for future reference.

The fire was in full flow and a welcoming heat greeted them. They sat down and were soon tucking into a nice hot cup of tea and scrumptious biscuits. Slowly the fire broke down the turf into fine white ash which collected below in the grate.

"This fresh air doesn't half make me tired Lorna."

"Yeah, me too Graham," Lorna replied, breaking into an enormous yawn. It wasn't long before the open fire started to work its hypnotising magic and they both started to nod.

After a few minutes of dozing off and waking again they accepted defeat and headed for bed. Apprehensively, they gazed outside the window, conscious of the previous night's visitor. Fortunately enough, only the unbroken darkness appeared outside the window and they settled down for the night and fell fast asleep.

Later that night Graham woke startled; he was convinced he had heard a noise. The room was dark with no natural light. Looking at his watch he could distinguish the luminous green arms, it was three o'clock in the morning. Creak! The bedroom door opened ever so slightly, Graham's heart started to beat harder.

"Lorna, are you awake?" he whispered through the door but there was no reply.

Graham tried to convince himself it was probably his imagination after the previous day.

"Lorna," he whispered louder through their joining door, but still no reply came. Graham felt isolated and vulnerable.

Again the door creaked but this time it was definitely opening wider.

Graham lifted the sheets above his head, noticing how loud his breathing was. He was convinced it was loud enough to reveal his location.

A footstep softly moved inside the room, shortly followed by another. He tried to hold his breath, hoping he would not be heard or noticed lying still in the bed.

The steps slowly moved towards his bed. Graham couldn't hold his breath any longer and gasped. He quickly turned in the bed hoping the intruder would be alarmed that he was stirring but still the steps moved further into the room.

He slowly peered above the sheets; his eyes were struggling to adjust to the darkness. Suddenly an image could be seen just at the bottom of his bed.

"Arrgh!" Graham screamed, unable to contain himself any longer.

The intruder, visibly shocked, fell backwards and a familiar voice shouted.

"Ow, my toe!" It was his Uncle.

Relieved, Graham shouted. "What are you doing Dan?"

"I heard a noise and came to check you were OK," he said, now noticeably holding his toe and starting to move towards the bedroom door.

Suddenly a large crash was heard, this time it came from outside.

Lorna, now awake with the goings on, jumped out of bed and swiped open the curtains.

They could just make out the image of the strange creature in a cloak jumping over the rear wall and off towards the old cemetery.

Lorna said: "That's him again, do you get the impression we're being watched?"

"Yeah, someone has a lot of interest in us," Graham replied, regaining his composure.

"Come on, let's go and find out what he wants," Lorna suggested.

"Maybe we should go and look tomorrow; it's the middle of the night," Graham quickly replied, satisfied he did not need any more excitement for the remainder of the night.

Lorna agreed, having second thoughts about going out. They both turned round to get back into bed when they noticed the image of Dan hopping past their bedroom door holding his foot.

After eventually falling asleep, Graham was woken by the succulent smell of freshly cooking sausages, immediately tantalising his taste buds. He jumped out of bed and moved quickly into the kitchen, noticing everybody else was up and eating breakfast.

"Morning," he said, pulling a chair up to the table, his hair dishevelled and his eyes heavy.

"Afternoon," replied Lorna, grinning broadly.

Graham's mother passed him some sausage, bread and a cup of tea.

"Shall we head over to the abbey and cemeteries after breakfast?" Lorna asked, not allowing Graham to start his breakfast.

"Hmm," replied Graham, stuffing his mouth with a juicy Irish sausage and nodding his head.

Following a satisfying breakfast they headed out onto the country lane and into the warm morning sunshine. The sounds of the country filled the air; the cows were braying and the swallows chattered gleefully as they flew dangerously close to the ground, occasionally changing direction suddenly in mid-air to catch a fly.

They passed the local shop and the old abbey came into view.

"What will we do if we see the cloaked fiend?" Graham asked guardedly.

"I will punch him on the nose!" replied Lorna defiantly.

"Yeah, did you see his nose last time?"

"Well no," replied Lorna, now starting to think about the implications.

Bobbing up and down on the top of some ruins, several crows cackled mischievously as they passed.

"What is this place Graham?" Lorna asked as they approached the entrance.

"They call it the Glebe; it was built sometime in the eighteenth century. The priest arrived from somewhere in America, one day he just disappeared. Some of the locals think he returned home but no one really knows what happened to him.

"The church was left and it gradually decayed over time."

They progressed down the footpath towards the old abbey, passing a man motionless with his head bowed by a gravestone. The proud abbey was now a shadow of its former glory, slabs of stone appeared white, perished by the ravages of time. Some of the solid walls had disintegrated over time and what remained was smothered by layers of thick suffocating Ivy. Some of the stones had fallen or been removed from the wall only to be used as gravestones years later.

There was ivy covering one complete side of the abbey and you could make out some arches from old doorways or windows just protruding from the ground. Just over the stone wall a few feet away you could see mounds in the field with grass grown over. These must have been even older structures which nature had reclaimed in time and there was a large circle of rocks like those at the bottomless lake.

Reaching the old abbey, they noticed a small entrance under one of the old arches. Somebody had placed a metal gate on it to prevent access to the inside of the structure. However, the gate was slightly ajar and a broken lock lay on the ground.

Without hesitation Lorna was on her hands and knees, the entrance was very low and access was gained by crouching right down. Lorna pushed the gate and it opened with a laboured noise as if it had been neglected for years.

She crawled, resting on the crunching gravel, which left several dimples in her skin. Disappearing out of sight, Graham decided to quickly follow, breathing deeply with great anticipation as he entered the old ruins.

Inside the ruins, the blue sky could be seen above as if looking up from the bottom of a large chimney breast; there were rocks strewn on the ground amongst the loose gravel. The ivy was growing on the inside of the rocks, reaching into every crevice, swallowing large areas of the walls. Inside the structure it was peaceful, in fact it was deadly silent, and no sound seemed to penetrate inside.

"You two should not be in here," said a deep and frightening voice.

They quickly looked round and blocking the entrance was a dark-haired man.

Standing six feet tall, and with enormous shoulders, his face looked as though it had seen battle many times before and had a large scar on his right cheek which reached from his beard to his ear. Haunting, motionless brown eyes were set deep into their sockets spaced evenly apart. A well-maintained black beard covered his rigid jaw line resembling Graham's old 'Action Man'. He wore dark creepy clothing; his black shirt had silver holes in it, where a small silver chain was laced through pulling the two sides of his shirt together. His jacket was black and about three-quarters the length of his body and they noticed a flash of something underneath as he moved his hand slightly. Sharp pointed spikes protruded dangerously from his leather wrist bands, designed to cause maximum damage.

"What are you doing in here?" he demanded in a chilling tone.

"L... l... looking around," Lorna stuttered, her arms straight down by her sides with her fingers pointing rigidly.

Graham started to edge around the monstrosity to see if the entrance was totally blocked. His heart started to thump faster as he realised they were trapped inside.

"You two could help me with a little problem I have, would you like to help me?" The air turned cold every time he spoke and chills ran down their spine. He pulled his coat back and there shining in the light was a sword.

"WELL YOU TWO, ARE YOU GOING TO HELP ME?" he said, shouting angrily and staring intently at them.

"Yes," Graham replied hesitantly. Slowly his eyes moved up and down the reinforced shaft until they came to rest on the handle. Rounded at the top it resembled the joint on a human bone. Shuddering with realisation, Graham's conclusion that it had no doubt been ripped from one of his victims and painstakingly polished. The fiend's fingers tapped menacingly on the handle to ensure attention was drawn to its origin.

"I have not seen a good friend, for what must be a century; it would be really good to see him again." Lorna noticed his teeth, they were black all around the edges, faded and decayed through years of neglect, or was he telling the truth about his age?

"He calls himself Carragah, do you know him?"

Graham and Lorna quickly glanced at each other; this man was bad and they had sensed that immediately.

"No, not heard of him," they replied, staring at this beast and there was silence.

He moved his mouth to reveal his rotten teeth and whispered "I think you know where he is". He took a step to the side to reveal someone else entering the ruins.

Moving towards them a figure started to edge into the ruins from the entrance. At first there wasn't much to see but a dark cloak but as he stood they noticed it was the masked faceless image which had been stalking them over the past two days.

Standing a few feet away they could not distinguish any facial features, just a dark empty image. Graham noticed his feet; they had three large toes or more like claws. Feeling very intimidated, they felt as if they were on a movie set resembling medieval times.

"Sucillian has been watching you; he is a good friend of mine." At this, the faceless being just bowed his head slightly in acknowledgement.

"I told you we don't know a Carragah!" Graham shrieked, panic stricken.

"You're lying to me. I know you met him yesterday and he informed you of the location of something precious to me!" he replied as he edged closer to Graham.

Lorna grabbed her friend's arm and they edged further back, crashing onto the cold stone wall. They were trapped with no where to go.

"LEAVE THEM ALONE!"

Appearing from nowhere, Lepy moved through the doorway towards the children, his boots crunching the loose gravel; he gave them a reassuring glance as he stood next to them. Although Graham and Lorna were relieved to see Lepy, his small stature against these monsters did little to alleviate their fears.

"Be gone with you, this is not your concern leprechaun," shouted the large intruder, moving his coat back to reveal his sword and placing his hand on it provocatively.

Lepy was not deterred; he nodded slightly still trying to reassure Graham and Lorna in their visibly petrified state.

"I warn you leprechaun, leave us now or your fate will be the same as your clans!" he demanded chillingly.

In response, Lepy pulled out a small glass ball and held it in his hand. The monster laughed and slowly started to draw his long, cold, steel sword, which scraped menacingly against its sheath.

Instantly, Lepy's glass ball exploded, intense sunlight blinded the threatening creatures; they flinched and covered their eyes, startled.

There was a pull on Lorna's arm and she followed instinctively, her eyes were blurred with a ball of bright white light imprinted on her retina. Suddenly everything went dark and Lorna landed heavily on her backside.

"What happened?" she screamed.

"It's OK," Lepy replied, reassuringly touching her shoulder as she lay on the ground. "We fell through a trap door and into the secret passageway."

Just behind where Graham landed, a light appeared. He looked round to see Lepy holding up his light ball and they could see again.

"Did you see that Graham?" Lorna exclaimed, excitedly.

"Lepy dazzled those things and then opened the secret passage, pushed us down and then closed it. Good move Lepy; you're a pretty cool leprechaun."

"Right you two follow me, we need to keep moving, it won't take Iroquois long to realise what happened."

Quickly walking off, Lepy looked back and indicated for them to hurry and follow.

Without hesitation they quickly started to follow, crouching down in the restricted passage, with the exception of Lepy, occasionally crawling through small gaps where the ceiling had started to collapse. It was dark, cold and the air was stale, reminding Lorna of the sewers back home, fortunately without the rats.

After a silent few minutes they noticed a small glimpse of light which steadily grew as they drew nearer. Lepy stopped just as they reached the exit. Graham noticed it was a doorway which was three-quarters blocked and only the top quarter was open. Lepy climbed through without any problems. Lorna managed to squeeze through tightly and then it was Graham's turn. He put his head through and his shoulders just managed to get through. With quite a lot of huffing and breathing in heavily, Graham tried to pull his waist and tummy through. Lorna stood towering above, reaching down she grabbed his hands and he was free. Climbing to his feet and scanning the surroundings, Graham declared,

"I know where we are. Uncle Jim showed me this place before, it's a secret passageway from the old abbey. It was built to protect the old monks from the Viking raids, never thought I would have used it for real."

Chapter 9

Heroic Actions

"COME, WE MUST MOVE QUICKLY," DEMANDED LEPY, "it won't be long before Iroquois and Sucillian realise what happened back there. Sucillian has probably been watching you since your arrival in Ireland and almost certainly knows you have been visiting Knocknakil. Carragah will be waiting for us, we must hurry!"

Lepy quickly paced away, turning briefly "Come on, hurry. We don't have much time".

He led them down by the farmhouse where Kathleen was busy working away in the garden, so busy she never noticed them passing by following a leprechaun. Lorna chuckled, watching Lepy ducking behind the odd obstacle and moving so quickly his legs could hardly support his body. What made it even more amusing was the fact nobody could see him anyway.

Lepy's pace was relentless, considering his stature, moving extremely quickly leaving the children struggling to keep up.

They progressed past the chicken sheds where Graham noticed something on the floor.

"Stop, wait there!" he demanded and quickly ran back towards the shed.

As he approached the shed his heart started pounding robustly. Slowly opening the door he lost his breath slightly, just there on the floor in front of him was a dead chicken, bloody feathers scattered all over. Graham noticed that something had killed the chicken and partly eaten its chest. There were several chickens sitting quietly on their nests. Under normal circumstances these chickens would have stampeded out when he entered the shed.

"What's up?" Lorna asked as she approached Graham, looking over his shoulder and noticing the gory carcass.

Gasping, she raised her hand to her mouth feeling like she was about to vomit and quickly turned away. After a few seconds she regained her composure,

"Bloody hell, what's happened here Graham, was it a fox?"

Lepy entered and responded. "No, that's no fox that's done this; a fox would have attacked the others as well. Whatever did this has only eaten part of the chicken, the fox would have taken all of it. I think we have trouble, we must move." And Lepy pushed Graham and Lorna quickly out of the shed.

"Why, what was it Lepy?" Graham shouted, quickly trying to catch up with Lepy who had already started to pull away.

"I can't be sure, probably a Shrake, which is bad news because they've come out from below the ground. We really must hurry, come on!"

Lepy was now moving again at pace and edging away from the youngsters.

Noticing some hefty thick bushes along a stone ridge he said "Ah just what we need". They were prickly blackthorn shrubs with spindly branches that appeared to be exploding in all directions.

Quickly approaching them, Lepy pulled two branches apart and jumped right into the middle, trying his best to avoid the sharp spines. Pulling and snapping at the sharp pointed branches he resurfaced a minute later.

"There you go," he announced, holding aloft the result of his toil, two thick sticks.

He handed one to Lorna and the other to Graham.

Lorna looked at Graham, "Walking sticks?" Graham just nodded, not really sure what to make of it.

"When the time comes you will know what to do with them," Lepy replied, setting off quickly again.

The sticks were black, with a small tilt where they had been snapped off, which conveniently worked as a handle, and small sharp notches protruding dangerously down the shaft.

"Get down now! " Lepy shouted in a sharp voice.

They dived to the floor taking cover. "What is it Lepy?" Lorna whispered.

"Sch... look over there near the stream." They both lifted their heads slightly and their hearts sank as they noticed three Shrakes stalking around the stream close to where the swallow hole was.

Their pointed ears were erect and their penetrating red eyes were menacingly searching the surroundings.

"What are they doing?" Graham whispered.

"Searching." Lepy replied. Reluctantly Graham continued swallowing hard,

"What are they searching for?"

"Us," Lorna whispered, realising the extreme danger they were in, her eyes glazed and fixed watching them quickly scouring the terrain.

Then a scream penetrated across the farm land, shrieking, announcing an unearthly presence had arrived. Graham instantly recognised the noise as that he had heard the night his Uncle Jim had passed away.

They looked to the direction of the scream. Just appearing over the hill in the distance emerged Sucillian; he was floating slightly above the ground so the rough landscape did not hinder his progress.

"Lepy look!" Graham shouted pointing in the direction of the distant hill, to the fast approaching Sucillian.

Lepy immediately reacted. "Graham and Lorna listen, I want you to do exactly what I say." His animated hand signals and the pitch of his voice left Graham and Lorna in no doubt the danger they were in.

They listened intently to his instructions. "When I give you the sign, go, and don't look back." Lepy jumped up and ran down the right hand side of the hill and jumped onto the stone wall a short distance away.

Crouching down on the wall he slowly crawled forward in the direction of the stream, looking up every few seconds.

Just on the bank of the stream one of the Shrakes stopped in its tracks and lifted its nose, the black wet nostrils retracted, smelling something in the air. Another scream penetrated the summer air as Sucillian passed over the first hill.

Graham looked at Lorna shaking his head. "We're trapped Lorna, why did I listen to you this morning!" he continued, in a derisive manner. "Let's go find the cloaked man," he continued sarcastically, his fears starting to get the better of him.

"Yeah, sorry about that Graham, not the best idea I've ever had," she replied, her hands expressing her thoughts.

Suddenly the Shrake who was picking up the scent bounded in Lepy's direction, increasing his speed with each leap. Simultaneously, Sucillian flew purposely towards the outnumbered Leprechaun. Graham and Lorna stooped behind some rocks, hoping that Lepy's plan would work.

The Shrake's fangs protruded from its mouth, showing its intent. Sucillian released another awful sickening scream as he quickly advanced upon his victim.

Just as they closed in on him his shout filled the air "Now Graham, now!!!"

Although their instinct was to remain hidden, something inside drove them up and seconds later Graham and Lorna were up and running.

Retreating down the hill their momentum quickly escalated towards the safety of the stream. Graham glanced back just as a Shrake leaped upon the wall attacking their last line of defence.

"No!" screamed Graham, unable to control himself, just as they disappeared over the other side of the wall.

The other Shrakes, hearing the cry, quickly turned, noticing Graham near the stream.

Within seconds they changed direction, accelerating vigorously towards them, their menacing fangs protruding as they approached Graham and Lorna. Immediately they gasped, running away was not an option with the speed of the approaching beasts. Leaping forward, the first arrived, launching at Lorna's neck.

She lifted her newly-acquired walking stick, with the movement of a baseball player she swung and connected directly with the leaping creature. It let out a huge cry and fell onto his back stunned.

The second attacker launched towards Graham, its claws preparing to strike. Graham took a step backwards and swung his blackthorn stick with all his might. He felt a large impact as the stick hit home with clinical precision.

"So that's what the sticks are for," shouted Lorna, satisfied she had seen off the Shrakes.

"Quick, run before they get back up!" Graham ordered. Instantly, he lurched forwards, quickly followed by Lorna.

Another loud shriek blasted Graham's eardrums; he stopped running and looked towards the origin of the noise and noticed Sucillian changing direction quicker than the wind. Immediately, Sucillian was airborne and closing in astonishingly fast.

"Graham, come on!" Lorna shouted, pulling urgently at his arm.

They both turned, running as fast as they possibly could towards the stream. Graham glanced back and noticed the cloaked danger closing in faster than they could run.

Breathing frantically, Graham started running as fast as humanly possible, his balance was becoming precarious as he quickly passed over every bump.

Again he glanced back, noticing Sucillian almost upon him, his sharp claw-like hands appeared from under his cloak ready to attack. Looking back, the safety of stream was only a few yards away.

"Jump Graham!" Lorna demanded and they both jumped together towards the safety of the water.

As Graham's feet started to penetrate the water he let out a huge scream as a sharp stabbing pain derived from his right shoulder.

Sucillian caught Graham digging his sharp claw deep into his flesh, instantly stopping his descent into the water and holding him aloft in mid air.

Graham flapped with his hands looking upwards straight into the dark gaze of Sucillian. His elbow caught his claw and Sucillian lost his grip.

Falling backwards Graham watched helplessly as it approached for a second attack, his claw prized ready to strike. An almighty splash engulfed his body and he submerged, falling deep into the water.

He drifted downwards and the bubbles bounced all around his body and it went dark.

Opening his eyes, Graham was relieved to notice the welcome sight of Carragah and Lorna standing there waiting for him in the cave.

"Are you OK Graham?" Lorna asked, her dark wide eyes sorry and watering slightly, which she quickly wiped, hoping no one had noticed. "I thought he had you."

"Yeah I thought so."

"You don't look so good," she continued, pointing at his shoulder.

Graham looked down and noticed his t-shirt was ripped and blood was coming from a wound.

"Come Graham, let's clean you up," Carragah suggested.

"What about Lepy I don't think he's made it. He was attacked by a Shrake, he used himself as a decoy so we could get here," Graham spurted out, not taking a breath, his heart heavy, thinking about the sacrifice Lepy had made to save them.

"I know but let's concentrate on you for now," Carragah said quietly and reassuringly.

"Oh no, I lost my blackthorn stick," Graham cursed.

"Drat, so have I, must have dropped it in the stream," Lorna realised.

"Not to worry, there are plenty of blackthorn bushes around," Carragah assured them.

Quietness fell on the cave and the three of them were left with their own thoughts about brave Lepy. Graham's head dropped as he replayed over in his mind the vicious animal launching his attack.

They followed Carragah in silence to the circular room they had entered the previous day.

"Please sit Graham, I will look at your shoulder," Carragah said, pointing at the nearest chair. Graham winced as he sat, the sharp pain in his shoulder escalated.

Carragah pulled away his t-shirt and Graham saw for the first time a large cut on the top of his chest.

"Quite a nasty wound that Graham. It just so happens I have the right treatment for a wound like that," and he pulled a small canister from his pocket and dipped his long finger in some shiny cream.

Graham was starting to feel a little queasy and decided not to look.

Carragah slowly rubbed the cream along the length of the wound and it started to heal. Lorna watched intently, although feeling nauseous, she just couldn't turn away as the blood retracted back into the wound and the skin knitted back together until all that was left was a small scar,

"Wow, that really works!" exclaimed Graham, moving his shoulder in a circular movement.

Carragah turned and sat on one of the chairs at the round table. Looking at Graham he started to speak.

"What bravery for a creature of such small stature, he is a true warrior,"

"No doubt Sucillian will know there is a connection to Knocknakil and the stream, it won't take him long to work out the rest. When he locates me he also finds the secrets hidden in the burial grounds that have lay hidden and at peace for over a thousand years. I am now getting older and weaker. I alone, cannot defeat him.

"To defeat this tyrant will require bravery and people who believe in good over evil. As I said before, it is no coincidence that you two have come to me. It is because you two young achievers, untouched by evil, are to defend these grounds at all costs. The time has come for me to show you the burial chambers. No one should ever enter these ancient chambers and ever discuss them with anyone. You cannot be sure that everybody is as they seem. I trust in you both but honestly don't know how you can defeat Iroquois. The only thing I can really tell you is he won't stop; he will never stop following you to the ends of the earth until he finds what he is looking for. Your shoulder looks better now Graham. Come, follow me, we have a lot to do but I'm afraid we don't have much time in which to do it."

Chapter 10

Burial Chambers

THE DOOR SHUDDERED AND THEN HURLED OPEN, **Lepy staggered into the** round room.

"Are you OK?" gasped Lorna, relief written all over her face.

"Not too bad, I forgot how fast those little suckers could be. Anyway, that one won't be bothering us again," Lepy replied as a wry smile appeared on his face.

Graham quietly assessed Lepy, noticing some scratches on his arm, he appeared to be relatively unscathed and he let out a huge sigh of relief. Within seconds he felt like a sudden weight had lifted off his shoulders which eased the tension on his heavy conscience.

"Everything OK Lepy?" Carragah asked.

"Yes, he put up a bit of fight but nothing I couldn't handle. That Sucillian was very close though, I noticed what happened with Graham."

Carragah did not respond; he walked towards the door at twelve o'clock, stood there for a few seconds and then turned one of the torches on the wall sideways. Instantly, the floor started to shake, dust and rock fell from the ceiling engulfing the whole room. A large rumble vibrated, shaking the very foundations of the underground cave and replicating a large earthquake. The children fell to their knees as if praying the earthquake would pass. Dust increased, filling the torch-lit room and restricting Graham's view as he frantically tried to peer around the room only for his eyes to be bombarded by thousands of little particles of earth. Recklessly he fought to keep them open against the onslaught.

Slowly the flickering candles fighting against the blitz started to win the battle.

Gradually Lorna, wiping the minute specks from her mouth, started to notice a short spiral staircase created by the fallen rocks.

Carragah descended the stairs, fell to his knees and grabbed something, holding it tight in his hands. He moved away from the vault and then climbed back into the room.

As the dust cleared, Graham observed him holding a small iron Celtic cross. It appeared old and in poor condition yet Carragah treasured it close to his chest.

"We will wait until the summer sun is near dusk before venturing out to avoid any unwanted attention," he said, sitting at a chair.

Sometime later the three of them followed him silently back through the swallow hole and back onto the farm. Carragah led them across the many hills on the farm land, leaving behind the now tranquil stream, still tightly clutching his prized possession. The friesians watched cautiously as they passed, their tails flicking tirelessly against the incoming insects.

Passing one of the many trees sporadically spread out on the farm, a rush of energy came over Lorna and she jumped grabbing a branch snapping it off.

"LORNA!" Carragah shouted, quite clearly infuriated.

Instantly she looked around, unclear as to the reason for the reprimand, nervously her dimples twitched as the anticipation built.

The stern look in Carragah's eyes eventually faded as he realised how nervous she was and wise compassion returned.

"Lorna, it's a trait I cannot understand, why did you snap that branch?"

"I dunno, it's just a tree."

"No Lorna, it's not just a tree, it's part of the delicate balance of nature. It allows us to breath, build and keep warm. Drawing off the land's natural energy sources they can actually be an ally…" Noticing Lorna's nervous and blank look he decided the rest could wait and he turned and walked away.

"Lecture," Lorna said sarcastically, a little embarrassed.

Silently they bypassed the farmhouse which was quiet with no sign of the owner. Through the gates they passed until they arrived at the ancient stone circle. Turning to Graham he spoke softly. "You three wait here, I won't be long!"

He walked into the primeval circle as the sun was starting to reach the last stages of its journey.

"What's he doing Lepy?" Lorna demanded, slowly starting to edge forward to get a better view and not waiting for an answer.

Carragah kneeled against one of the rocks and started to speak in an unfamiliar tongue. "Tain ke awth."

"Now what's he saying!" Lorna barked, fleetingly looking at Lepy.

"Wait here!!" ordered Lepy and Lorna stopped still in her tracks, stunned by the tone of the leprechaun's voice.

Carragah lifted the small cross which was only slightly larger than his hand up into the air as he continued his ritual.

Graham noticed a carving on the largest rock where Carragah knelt; it was a small Celtic cross just like the one the druid priest was holding.

"Do you know what he's doing, Lepy?" Graham politely asked.

"It's an old Celtic ritual, my grandfathers used to tell me tales about them. I have never witnessed one until now; this is probably the first ritual in these parts for hundreds of years."

"Wow, cool," Lorna shouted, gazing over at the ancient priest, "a real life ritual."

The ancient priest's cloak flapped gently in the breeze. Holding the cross in front of him, he placed it into the recess on the rock. Four clasps, which were hidden in the stone, snapped at each point of the cross, holding it in place.

"It is nearly time, we must now wait for the sun to set" explained, looking up at the sky.   in her hands

"Why, what happens then?" Lorna asked a little

"Have patience my friend, all will be reveal

Lorna grunted and sat on another roc
like a bored schoolgirl.

"Tell me Graham, how is that shoulder of yours?" Carragah asked, pointing in his direction.

"I forgot all about it, it feels a lot better thanks to you," Graham replied, prodding it with his hand. A deep sense of gratitude and fondness grew in Graham's heart as he warmed to this mysterious man who until yesterday was an old Irish tale.

The August sky started to turn pink as the sun lowered in the sky. Carragah rose to his feet and moved behind the largest rock which was about the same height as him.

Graham, Lorna and Lepy watched as the sun descended towards the ocean. Slowly it passed by the rocks and just as it met the horizon the sunlight shone through the stone circle shining directly through the two nearest rocks and landing on the furthest stone which housed the old iron cross.

At the centre of the antique cross a bright red light started to develop. Within seconds the scarlet glow was blinding; the party shielded their eyes. The rock trembled and Graham and Lorna watched in amazement as the cross slowly started to turn clockwise on its own.

Instantly, two of the large rocks where the beams of sunlight had shone through started rising. Large mounds of earth scattered, displaced by the momentum as they slowly climbed skywards. As they rose, a beam appeared horizontally across the two rocks which looked like the top of a doorway. Still the rocks ascended, revealing a secret entrance with a staircase descending deep into the ground. Eventually the rocks stopped moving as dust rose from the ancient doorway.

Slowly the cloud disbanded and a stone doorway caught the last rays of the sun as it fell sleepily from view.

"Would you be so kind as to lead the way?" Carragah asked, pointing appeared.

moved towards the entrance and removed his small globe
d it aloft inside the doorway and a brilliant light

"That light reveals secrets that are hundreds of years old!" Carragah said, moving slowly behind Lepy.

"Come," he said, beckoning to the children. Lorna cautiously moved forwards, giving Graham a friendly firm push so he went first.

"Hey, Lorna I bet hardly anyone has ever seen this place before!" Graham said in awe, satisfied yet deeply concerned about what lay ahead.

"Yes sure," Lorna replied a little dismissively, her hands holding Graham's waist as she peeped over his shoulder, using him as a human shield.

Moving slowly down the three flights of solid stone stairs, a short passageway was exposed with the dazzling light, heavy stone blocks purposely placed on top of each other to create the chamber.

Quietly, the fearless leprechaun piloted the party through an archway at the bottom of the flights of stairs. As Graham passed through he noticed three chambers, one leading left, another right, the third declined at a steep angle deeper into the ground.

"What do the inscriptions say?" asked Lepy, pointing to some writing above the third entrance.

Carragah studied them carefully. "It's a very old dialect; I think it says 'grounds are sacred, death'. Sorry, I can't make the rest out!"

"No, no it's fine, don't bother," Lorna interrupted, clutching Graham a little harder.

"I do remember some legends about a ghostly warrior," Carragah continued.

Lorna and Graham looked at each other apprehensively as colour drained from their cheeks, feeling the heavy melancholy deep in their body.

Carragah pointed into the chamber on the left and ushered them to go through and look inside.

"Erm, no it's OK Carragah," Lorna replied a little dismissively.

"You will be fine," he replied, pushing his hands forwards as if he was ushering the cows.

Graham swallowed deeply, wondering why he was accepting the challenge, maybe it was just trust.

"I hope we don't see that warrior or I'll have a heart attack!" Lorna said, linking Graham's arm even tighter, practically stopping his blood supply.

Slowly and a little braver with Lorna clasping him, Graham edged towards the arched dark entrance. The arch reminded Graham of old castles he had visited on school trips but his pounding heart ensured he knew this was for real.

There was no light inside the chamber and Graham stood still, even with Lorna trying to push him forward.

"Here, I think this will help," Carragah said, handing Graham a torch.

Graham smiled as he instantly recognised the torch as a modern battery-operated torch.

"Well this is the twenty-first century!" Carragah smiled, moving away.

"Come on then Graham!" Lorna said impatiently, giving him a little nudge in the direction of the doorway.

"You go first Lorna," Graham replied, trying to hand the torch to Lorna.

"No way!" she replied, keeping her firm grip of his arm.

Graham switched on the torch and the beam shone deep into the entrance. He took a deep breath as he put his first foot forward.

It was really spooky as they entered, cobwebs hanging from the ceiling brushed against Graham's face, making him jump for a brief second.

They slowly edged each other forward until they were several feet inside the chamber. Lorna looked back and there was no reassurance of Lepy or Carragah, they were now on their own.

Graham shone the torch around the dark chamber, lighting up isolated sections because of its size as it moved around.

"Wow, look at that, we're rich!" shouted Lorna with delight as the torch revealed large chests full of treasure. Gold and silver chalices and plates, along with thousands of small coins. Brilliantly-coloured brooches with large precious stones inset into the gold, which reflected invitingly to Lorna. She started to move forward, confidence now starting to increase. The torchlight lifted slightly, revealing a large stone coffin, immediately behind the treasure. Graham froze, the beam from the torch slowly moved along the length of the stone tomb.

"That's carved out of the stone!" gasped Graham, whispering so not to disturb the deceased.

"Unbelievable, it must have taken ages," Lorna replied, still tightly linking Graham's arm.

"Look at the slab on the top; it's slightly open, shine the torch inside Graham," Lorna urged, stepping behind her accomplice.

Graham moved the torch towards the gap as Lorna's grip intensified.

"Watch it, Lorna!" Graham shouted, reacting nervously.

The beam entered the coffin briefly. "No, it's not right!" Graham declared, moving briskly away.

The shaft of light moved around the room and came to rest.

After a few seconds they started to register what it had revealed.

"Ahh... it's a skull!" Lorna screamed. The light revealed a skeleton, lying next to an open treasure chest revealing more coins.

Lorna again pulled on Graham's arm. He was already off balance and they fell heavily onto the stone floor.

Screaming, they both scrambled out of the chamber fighting against each other to be first out.

CRASH!!

"Watch it you two!" Lepy shouted as they all collided with him and landed on the floor.

"That's what happens to grave robbers," Carragah said, signalling for them to stand.

"Time has long forgotten the name of the king of Knocknakil who lies peacefully in there. Judging by the treasure and guards he was very influential.

"We must hurry – time is against us." Carragah lifted Lepy to his feet and they moved away under the guidance of Lepy's light.

Moving down the steep passageway towards another chamber, Lepy and Carragah led the way.

Lepy lifted his globe as he entered the chamber; a huge cavern revealed itself for the first time in centuries. Carragah led the way, moving steadily down three flights of stairs.

Graham looked and noticed how large the cavern was; the ceiling spanned far beyond the glare of Lepy's light. Around the sides of the cavern were numerous arches carved out of the rock which were dark and uninviting. Carragah raised his hand and several torches ignited along the frames of the arches, increasing the forbidding dark archways. The underground expansion reluctantly relinquished its veiled cavity to foreign eyes. Reaching the bottom of the steps, a stone bridge stretched over a bleak depression. Cautiously, the children inched forward, only too aware there was no protection should they slip off the narrow walkway and tumble to the centre of the earth. The atmosphere was crisp, only the sound of dripping water and their own footsteps brought any life to the stillness.

Stepping off the bridge they were greeted by a floor of long stone slabs carefully placed in rows, stretching from one side of the arches to the other.

"Bloody hell, have you seen in there?" Lorna shouted, just managing to see in the nearest arch. Graham strained his eyes and noticed a wooden box which had disintegrated over time, exposing a skeleton.

"You didn't warn me about that Lorna!" Graham gasped, his breath deserting him for a second with shock. Silently they glanced where the flickering light permitted, to be greeted with the same sight in other rounded gateways. After several more steps, Carragah stopped and turned looking down at the children, his eyebrows retracting closer together to relay a serious message. Pointing down towards the stone floor he said: "This is where those chosen to protect this place lie."

Graham, following Carragah's direction, noticed an indentation in the ground. Taking a step forward, he stared down several feet where a large solid stone sarcophagus had been carved. Along its length a long sword had been placed, probably so the owner was never far away from his weapon.

"Graham, come and look at this!" Lorna exclaimed, pointing down at another depression. Graham quickly ran over. "It's the same as that one over there, look another," he continued as they noticed a third all spaced evenly next to each other.

"Oh, there's another, look at this one it's different to the others," Lorna shouted across at Graham and he quickly ran over. Just slightly ahead of the other three tombs lay another.

Graham noticed the sword on this coffin was slightly different, gold-handled with inscriptions at the top of the razor sharp blade.

"These are the protectors of the secret burial grounds," Carragah said, gazing downwards at the fourth tomb.

"Anybody brave enough to enter these chambers and access the spring has to pass this way at their own peril."

"Yeah, but they're dead." Lorna muttered.

Carragah looked up at Lorna, "Hmm".

However, before he could respond further, Lorna's attention had switched. Her eyes were fixed ahead with her jaw slightly open, totally focused. Graham, noticing the silence, looked up straight at Lorna. Immediately, he noticed her deep concentration but something more interesting caught his attention. Staring into her deep brown eyes he noticed a bright dancing reflection. Slowly, Graham turned around in the direction she was looking.

"WWWOW," Lorna exclaimed, her mouth remaining open as she moved closer. Graham edged forward, for a second he was speechless,

Staring ahead he could now see the origin of all natural energy on the planet and it was magnificent.

Chapter 11

Return of Iroquois

"That wasn't there a second ago," Graham said, looking at Carragah.

"Only when you pass these tombs can the spring be seen by any soul," he replied.

"I have never, ever, seen anything like this before!" Lorna replied smiling, gazing intently.

Graham's stare returned, watching the glorious light display right before his eyes.

At the end of the platform a large pool swirled spectacularly, reaching deep into the Earth's crust. Illuminating the cavern, the stunning lights radiated throughout that part of the cave.

Fantastic colours spun quickly, all imaginable shades spiralled downwards deep into the Earth's core, being pushed forward by an unseen force.

Graham watched intently, looking as far as his eyes could see as this tornado of light left him feeling mesmerised.

Streaks of silver danced with flashes of green and indigo. Quickly they spun deeper and deeper until they eventually faded from sight, only to be replaced by blue and pink in an unending cycle of energy. High around the sides the energy spun briskly before descending out of sight.

A gentle buzz filled the air, tickling the receptors in Graham's ear.

"Look at the hairs on my arm Graham!" Lorna said excitedly, looking at each one stood proudly as her body tingled with the sensation.

"Yeah, same here," Graham replied, his arms straight out vibrating with a nice tickling sensation.

"Hey, look at Lepy's hair!" Lorna grinned pointing at the leprechaun.

Glancing round, Graham saw his hair pointing skywards, reminding him of a hedgehog, much to the annoyance of his small friend.

Carragah moved forwards and down three steps leading down to the spring. Directing his staff, he dipped it into the whirlpool; after a few seconds he lifted it from the source. The small globe at the top of his stick shone brightly; it had captured some of the radiant light from the spring and he lifted it up, staring longingly at it. He turned to the others. "This energy draws from the sky and sea to supply the land with the power of sustaining life. Each and every living being from insect to human thrives on this source without realising its importance. Even the plants and trees draw from the endless supply completing the cycle of life. I am sure this will help us later," he said, looking at his companions still standing on the platform.

"Come, we must go," he said, beckoning for the others to follow.

Passing back by the coffins, Graham's curiosity got the better of him. "The sword on this tomb, it's different from the others," he said, looking at Carragah.

"Hmm... I thought you might ask, I do believe this sword belongs to a renowned warrior from these parts. Cuchulain."

"Never heard of him," Lorna instantly replied.

"Well young Lorna, that just may be because you're not a thousand years old."

"Graham, have you noticed the spring fading as we move away?"

"I don't think its fading, it just kind of blends in to the background," he replied, moving back towards it, watching it reappearing again.

As they left the burial chambers and returned back towards the entrance, Lorna noticed little red dots flickering around the staircase.

"Shrakes," shouted Lepy.

"We're trapped," replied Lorna.

In a matter of seconds there were three of them, with one leading at the front. He stopped just in front of Lepy, lifting his nose in the air sensing something. His red eyes were glowing brightly in the dark passageway.

Out of the darkness, two outlandish characters gradually appeared – Iroquois and Sucillian.

"Fine animals these Shrakes, could find a leprechaun anywhere in Ireland.

"You may go now, my little hell cats, good job, we will deal with it from here." They turned, screeching as they bounded away. "So these are the secret burial grounds then, I have waited a long time for this moment Carragah!" Iroquois said, moving closer to the chamber, pulling out his sword and pointing it in the direction of Lepy along with Graham and Lorna.

"Well I won't be needing you three now will I!" he said, becoming more menacing with his weapon.

Sucillian forced his way past the party and into the chambers, swiftly followed by Iroquois. "Three chambers, hmm..., maybe they might still be of use."

Instantly and without warning, Iroquois seized Lorna with an arm around her neck and a sword pointing at her soft stomach area. "It's over Carragah. I am in the secret chamber; just tell me which passage to follow. I promise if you co-operate your deaths will be fast and painless." Iroquois pushed the sword in slightly to Lorna's side. "Ahh!" Lorna shouted as the sword penetrated her skin slightly. The colour drained from her face, she stared in Graham's direction, unable to speak and he noticed how frightened she was.

"Don't worry, Lorna, I'll think of something," Graham replied, trying to be courageous.

Carragah looked across at Lorna and smiled. He was proud of her loyalty, not revealing the secret despite her life being in the balance.

"Lorna, you are brave and loyal, it's in there," Carragah said, pointing down one of the passages.

Immediately, Iroquois dropped Lorna to the floor and with the sword placed in the small of her back forced her towards the others and then down the passageway just behind Sucillian.

"Don't worry, I won't let him do anything to you!" Graham whispered. Lorna didn't respond, too frightened to talk with the sword pushing sharply in her back.

Sucillian fearlessly entered the first chamber and scanned all around. Iroquois slowly followed as if a little apprehensive, looking up and down the dark room and pushing Lorna into the chamber as he entered. "Maybe we need one of those kids to ensure there are no little surprises left," he said, noticing the skeleton. Sucillian was now fully in the tomb just next to the treasure. He bent down, looking intently at the skeleton and noticed a small Celtic cross clasped securely in its skeletal hand. Reaching to grab it, his claws wrapped around the cross and wrestled to release it.

"Don't touch it, Sucillian!!" Iroquois shouted with urgency, pushing Lorna back towards the others, as he entered deeper into the chamber, his rough voice echoed around the compartment.

Swoosh; a sudden flash of light came from the wall in the chamber. Graham flinched as he noticed an axe disappear back into the wall and quick gush of air blew his hair. Rapidly, Sucillian's bloodcurdling scream reverberated throughout the passageways and chambers as his lifeless cloak fell heavily on the stone floor.

"Run!" Carragah shouted, pushing Graham and Lorna out of the chamber.

"CARRAGAH!!!!!!!!" screamed Iroquois from the chamber. Graham glanced back and observed Iroquois holding his sword aloft and quickly turning in their direction. Graham turned, noticing the others had already left the chamber and quickly started running up the three flights of stairs. His legs were heavy and slow and Iroquois started to catch him up. Glancing back, Iroquois was only a few feet away and had his sword held aloft ready to deliver the killing blow. Graham put his head down, running as fast as possible. Feeling the heavy breath on his neck he was just contemplating surrender when Carragah's voice broke the silence.

"Leave the boy be, Iroquois!" Graham started to dip his head to gain more speed but found his balance compromised and he fell heavily onto his front as he passed the last step and out of the entrance. Two large boots crushed rocks either side of Graham and he turned onto his back and peered upwards where Iroquois was now stood like a mountain.

Iroquois smiled a chilling, awful smile which exposed his black decaying teeth. His calculated eyes gazed into Graham's,

"Who's going to save you now!" he said menacingly as his sword jerked violently towards Graham's head. Lorna screamed, her hands clasping her cheeks in horror as she felt her heart sink.

As it entered the final stages of its descent, a large flash from Carragah's staff shot through the air like a lightning bolt, striking Iroquois on the chest, catapulting him violently on the floor and instantly stopping the progression of his sword.

Lepy grabbed the Celtic cross from the stone, twisting it anti-clockwise. The tomb shook as the two rocks housing the entrance quickly descended, concealing the entrance. Iroquois lay on his back, his arms spread out and still clutching his sword but he appeared lifeless.

Carragah grabbed Graham by the arm and lifted him.

"Is he dead?" Graham asked, his heart pounding heavily.

"No, only dazed, come we must go before he awakes," replied Carragah, pulling Graham away.

"Lepy, we must return the cross to its secure vault," Carragah said, taking the cross back off the leprechaun and securely fastening it inside his cloak.

Graham glanced across at Lorna and noticed her eyes were watering; he went across and held out his hand. She smiled as she placed her hand in his and felt a little safer as they quickly moved away from the stone circle.

"Wake up!" Gregorian grunted, kicking Iroquois in the side. "I am sure the Boggot would not be happy with you falling asleep."

Iroquois' eyes opened slowly and he clambered to his feet, noticing Gregorian with his lieutenant Guthrum.

"Where are the rest of your men?" Iroquois demanded.

"They are at Devil's Point awaiting your instructions!"

"Good, get your men and track down Carragah and his miniature army!" he ordered.

Gregorian nodded his head acknowledging the order and turned to return to his ship.

"Oh Gregorian, nobody harms them but me!"

"Of course," he nodded, turning away again.

"Guthrum, you come with me, we have a leprechaun to catch," Iroquois continued.

Guthrum smiled. "With pleasure," he replied, a sly smirk spreading from cheek to cheek.

Iroquois let out a loud sustained whistle which quickly spread across the deserted countryside.

Within seconds, little reds dots could be seen flickering in the distance. Then the black cats appeared from the dark air.

"Go, find them, this time you can do what you want to the leprechaun!" Iroquois pointed and they bounded off screeching, with himself and Guthrum quickly following.

The moon was bright and peaceful, allowing the party some guidance now their eyes had adjusted to the darkness.

"What was that noise?" Lorna asked, hearing a whistle break the silent air.

"That's Iroquois, come it won't take long for him to find us," Carragah replied, urging them forward.

They picked up their pace, running as fast as the night light would allow across the broken ground. Graham stumbled for what could have been the seventeenth time which amused Lorna who used Graham as her personal guide.

A screech echoed eerily around, which sent cold shivers through the children, unable to establish where it was originating from.

"Shrakes have picked up our scent!" Lepy announced, his chest beating heavy from the hard running his little legs were doing.

"Come, don't stop. We are nearly there!" Carragah urged as Lepy now started to fall behind.

Another screech broke the silence, although this one seemed much closer.

"Quickly, into the swallow hole," Carragah shouted as the stream revealed its location under the moonlight.

"You go!" Lepy shouted.

Graham glanced back as Carragah and Lorna entered the water. Lepy had stopped some distance back and his hands were on his knees as his chest laboured from the exertion. He noticed just beyond his accomplice, the red dots as the Shrakes emerged hot on his tail. Without thinking Graham ran towards Lepy. "No Graham, save yourself!" Lepy shouted.

It was too late; Graham was running like an express train in his direction. The screeches became louder as the attackers quickly approached.

Graham grabbed his accomplice and turned towards the safety of the stream.

The screeches were inches away as he hurtled himself forward. Lepy tucked tightly under his arm looked back just as the nearest Shrake attacked, his claws coming together in a pincer movement.

Lepy kicked out, sweetly connecting with its jaw, and it rolled onto the floor colliding heavily with its counterparts.

Graham dived into the safety of the stream, still tightly clutching Lepy.

"You are a brave man, Graham!" Carragah said, greeting them both.

"Thanks," Lepy said, staring deeply at Graham, his eyes expressing the gratitude he felt.

Graham acknowledged by just smiling, a little surprised with himself.

"What about me!" Lorna shouted.

"You, too, are a brave woman!" Carragah replied, smiling at Lorna who was now looking very pleased with herself.

"I would have grabbed Lepy, it's just Graham was closest."

"Of course, Lorna, of course." Carragah turned and quickly prompted them to follow.

A short distance down the dark passageway Lorna noticed something ahead slouched against a wall.

"What's that?" she asked, pointing at her find.

"It looks like a skeleton of a large kind of beast," Graham replied with his best guess.

"It's a cow, or should I say it once was a cow," said Carragah. "Unfortunately, every year or so one would step on a swallow hole and end up down here. After roaming around for some time the Shrakes would eventually track it down. That meal would enable them to survive for the next six months."

"Carragahhh," echoed through the passageway.

"That's Iroquois and he sounds angry if you ask me!" said Lepy, looking in the direction of the voice.

"Time to go!" said Carragah.

"Yeah, good idea, but what about the key to the chambers?" Lepy replied.

"We will try and circle back later, it's too risky to open the vault now with Iroquois around," Carragah replied, sharply moving away.

Chapter 12

Devil's Point

THEIR PACE QUICKLY CHANGED INTO A JOG, a small dot appeared ahead of them in the distance. Moonlight was penetrating the passageway so there was a way out. Lepy navigated through all the fallen and loose rocks leading out of the tunnel.

There was a slight howl as Graham bounced onto a large rock; a fresh ocean gust blasted into his face, driving salt water onto his lips which he could taste instantly. It was a great sensation, the strong Atlantic wind shook his hair, leaving him liberated and for a short time free.

The ocean waves crashed against the jagged rocks, leaving white distinctive foam rising briefly in the air. The crisp white waves surged through the fresh dark air to repeat the sequence; the atmosphere was intensely mystifying as the moon urged the ocean to crash against the towering cliff.

"Graham," Lorna shouted, beckoning to her friend.

Glancing around, Graham noticed Carragah, Lorna and Lepy climbing up the rock face above. Realising he had slipped into a trance, reality soon returned and he quickly ran to catch up with them, slipping on a couple of loose rocks on the way. It was quite a steep climb; rocks were being knocked down by Lorna, narrowly missing Graham, much to his annoyance.

"Watch it, Lorna!" Graham shouted as another rock bounced narrowly just past him. Cautiously and against his better judgement, he peered over his shoulder as it crashed into hundreds of pieces on the jagged cliff face far below.

"Be careful, Graham!" Carragah warned.

Graham gasped as his heart started beating hard; there was no margin for error on this steep rock face with no barrier between him and certain death.

Lepy was now climbing over the ridge. Lorna's hand came down shortly afterwards and helped pull Graham to safety. "What a view!" Lorna exclaimed excitedly, pointing out towards the ocean, her dark brown hair blowing right across her face as she watched energetic wave after wave surge inland.

"Magnificent," Graham replied, scrambling away from the edge looking around.

"No time for sightseeing, we must keep moving!" demanded Lepy, ascending further.

"You're right, Lepy," Carragah shouted, ensuring his voice was heard over the thunderous Atlantic wind.

Graham and Lorna glanced at each other as another rock was knocked from above.

Standing there proudly on a slight incline was a ram; his horns were completely turned in on themselves and his wool all ragged and torn. He nodded his head a couple of times, showing his horns in all their glory and his intent to attack imminently.

"Stand over there!" ordered Lepy, taking control of the situation.

They followed his orders without question; taking orders from a mini leprechaun without even flinching an eye. The ram dropped his head and scraped his feet, accelerating in the blink of an eye he launched at Lepy. At the very last second, Lepy dropped to the floor, his low centre of gravity enabling him to drop below the despairing charge of the insane ram. The ram fought valiantly to regain his foothold with great determination and just as he regained it the last rock gave way. His cry carried on the wind for a few seconds and then fell silent. The rocks below had claimed him for the Atlantic. "Rams don't like us leprechauns," Lepy said, clambering to his feet.

Carragah led the way up the steep grass hillside littered with featureless rocks. Rams held their ground until the very last second, before darting further up the uneven mountainside.

The countryside was very harsh, only mountain sheep could survive this environment. Lepy stopped and looked back,

"Look at how high we are now!" he said, pointing down some considerable distance.

"Wow, I don't think I have ever climbed this high before," Lorna added, standing proudly.

Sudden movement caught her eye, she fought with the low light to see if she could identify what it was, again it quickly moved some distance below.

"What are those black specs moving down there?" Lorna continued.

"Shrakes!" shouted Graham as his heart sank.

"Now what do we do, we don't have our blackthorn sticks?" replied Lorna, lifting her hands.

Lepy paused for a few seconds, staring downwards as the shape of the Shrakes became clear.

"Quick, grab a rock!" Lepy ordered bending down to grab the nearest boulder.

He tussled to lift it above his head as if he was in an Olympic weightlifting competition.

With the satisfaction of breaking the Olympic record, he hurled it down the steep hill. It quickly picked up momentum and bounced with great bounds as it made its way down the hillside.

Lorna held her breath in anticipation as she watched the progress of this projectile; it bounced right over the Shrake.

"Ah, unlucky Lepy, have another go," Lorna shouted.

"Come on, you grab one too," Lepy shouted, struggling with his second.

"No way, there are loads of sheep droppings!" Lorna replied, holding her hands tightly together.

"I tell you what Lorna; you leave it to the Shrakes to get up here instead!" Graham replied, lurching a rock with a football throw.

"Oh, OK then," she replied picking up the smallest rock she could find.

Just exiting the passageway, another cat-like image appeared, followed immediately by another, and they started to run up the hill.

Graham launched his rock, stopping to see if it achieved its target. It homed in on its target which instantly changed direction, avoiding the impact. Hurriedly, they threw rocks but these beasts were so fast it appeared like an impossible task.

"Yes!" shouted Graham as a Shrake took a direct hit and collapsed to the floor.

"That was my shot!" Lorna exclaimed, frowning in Graham's direction.

Graham just smiled; satisfied her little rocks were not going to do much damage, as he quickly threw another.

"It's like ten-pin bowling, this," Lorna said, looking for her next bowling ball.

The Shrake that was hit was not moving and there were several rocks bouncing vigorously towards the other two. The nearest black image managed to dodge left as a large rock narrowly missed him, straight into the path of a much larger one. Crash, it landed right on top of him, violently pushing him back in the opposite direction.

"Yes, that was mine as well!" shouted Lorna, throwing her hand in the air as if she had scored a goal.

"No way, I'm claiming that one," replied Graham.

"We can discuss credit later, keep throwing," urged Lepy.

Determined, the remaining Shrake snarled as it dodged all incoming rocks with great agility.

"We're not going to get this one," shouted Lorna concerned, as she stared at the sharp fangs protruding menacingly; it sprang the last few feet to attack Lepy who was closest.

With his last effort before the imminent attack, Lepy threw a rock.

Bang, he was hit, but precariously the beast clambered back to his feet, shrugged his head and with his glaring red eyes launched at Lepy for the kill.

Crash, another rock hit his head; again it slowly gained control of his feet with great resolve and took a few steps forward. Whack! Again he went down; this time, blood started pouring from its head, it was fatally wounded.

"That was close," said Lepy, moving towards his victim.

"Good work you three. Iroquois won't be far away, we must move," Carragah said, starting to move up towards the summit.

"Did you see my shots, three out of three!" claimed Lorna.

Lepy looked at Graham and they both started laughing.

Ascending further up the rock face, Graham occasionally peeked, still memorised by the spectacular views.

"Does this hill never end, every time we get near the top another hill appears; it's never ending," whinged Lorna, her head drooping towards the floor.

"You do complain for a young lady Lorna," replied Carragah. "Try this walk when you're several hundred years old, like me," he continued.

Lorna didn't reply, choosing to conserve her energy.

Eventually reaching the ridge, Graham looked back to where they started their ascent.

"We must have climbed nearly a thousand feet to reach this ridge," Graham shouted, the wind still making it difficult for them to hear each other.

"Carragah, what's that over there?" Lorna asked, pointing down towards the ocean.

They could just distinguish a large rock the size of a house shrouded by low mist in a small bay silhouetted against the moonlight. It was a crystal clear night and visibility from their vantage point was unsurpassed; the only hindrance was a low dense mist hovering around this uninviting bay.

"That's Devil's Point, Lorna," Carragah replied.

"For centuries, Viking and pirate ships landed there; it is not a very nice place. The bay is littered with shipwrecks. During bad weather, pirates forced ships laden with treasure into the bay. The strong winds from the ocean would smash the wooden hulls to pieces. After the storms, the pirates would collect all the treasure and leave no survivors alive."

Just as they started to move off, Graham noticed some of the dense mist clear for a second.

"Did you see?" he said, looking to Lorna who had already moved away.

Graham's thoughts worked overtime; he was sure for a split second he saw something.

"We need to head south," Lepy replied, pointing in that direction. "Across that ridge and towards Crough Patrick in the distance."

"My legs are aching after climbing and walking for so long, I'm so hungry too," said a very glum-looking Lorna.

"Trust you to think of your belly!" Graham replied, rubbing his.

"I bet you're hungry too, Graham. We really should go home," Lorna said, hoping for Graham to agree.

"It's better to go back late rather than not at all," interrupted Carragah.

"You cannot return there tonight. Iroquois is certain to have someone watching over your place."

"Talking about watching, get down," shouted Lepy. They all dropped to the floor, looking around the empty fields. Lepy peeked over a large rock just ahead before quickly dropping back down. "There's one of Iroquois' soldiers over that ridge."

Graham stood cautiously; over the ridge he noticed what at first glance appeared to be a Viking soldier.

"Bloody hell, I was right!" he exclaimed, dropping to his knees.

"What is it Graham?" Lorna whispered.

"I was sure at Devil's Point I saw a Viking ship through the mist, you better check yourself," Graham replied.

Lorna peered slowly over and dropped instantly like Graham.

"It's a man dressed as a Viking," Lorna said, pausing for a few seconds.

He had thick metal armour on his chest, by his side was a round shield made from wood with spiky steel pieces set into it. Sharp pointed horns appeared to protrude from his helmet.

"Trust me, he is very real," Carragah said, after quickly looking himself. "Iroquois is a very influential and desperate man; he will stop at nothing to capture us.

"We must continue this way. Come on, follow me quietly. Be sure, this brute will not hesitate to kill or maim you!"

Graham gasped, realising the danger they were in. Lepy slowly started to crawl in the fiend's direction.

Slowly, with deliberate steps, Lepy edged down the opposite side of the stone wall where the man was guarding only two or three feet away. He turned and beckoned to the others to follow after successfully passing without a sound.

Time moved slowly as Graham slowly managed to pass without drawing any attention to himself and survive for at least a few more minutes.

Carragah urged Lorna to go. "No, I can't do it," replied Lorna, shaking her head; her hands were starting shake with apprehension.

"Well Lorna if you don't, Iroquois will be along shortly and believe me, he won't show you any mercy."

Lorna accepted her position, remembering the sword incident and slowly crawled forward. Pushing herself as tight to the wall as possible, she edged in the direction of Lepy and Graham. Her arms felt extremely heavy and she feared they would collapse under the weight of her body.

"She's too close to the wall," whispered Lepy in Graham's ear.

"Move out a little," Graham whispered motioning at Lorna.

"What?" Lorna replied silently, shrugging her shoulders. As her arm lifted it caught the dry stone wall and a small rock fell banging onto another.

Instantly, the guard heard the noise and leapt onto the wall, weapon drawn and his evil eyes scouring the dark countryside.

Chapter 13

The Bottomless Lake

T HE SOLDIER STOOD ON THE DRY STONE wall scouring the surrounding area for any signs of life. His thick set legs with knee length sandals were inches above Lorna's head. He walked along the wall towards Graham and Lepy who pushed themselves as close to the wall as possible.

Lorna noticed his sword swinging from side to side as the guard continued looking for the origin of the noise. Stopping above Lepy and Graham, he started to peer over the wall at the exact spot they were hiding.

Carragah noticed an owl sitting in a tree a short distance away. Placing his hands on the top of his staff he closed his eyes and they started to flicker as he fell into a deep trance.

Just as the soldier's view was about to reveal the helpless souls, the white owl swooped from the sky, screeching as it approached the unsuspecting warrior. In a flash his sword swung swiftly at the bird. Furiously the owl hurled its wings downwards creating enough draft to pull itself away from the cold steel.

Collapsing backwards from the momentum of his swing, the Viking fell off the wall. Instantly he was back on his feet scouring the sky for the surprise vigilante.

He stopped for a few seconds, gazing back across the wall but soon moved off looking skywards as he walked.

"Come quick," whispered Lepy, beckoning to Lorna and Carragah.

"Don't need to ask me twice," replied Lorna, finding new strength and moving sharply.

They all looked at Carragah who was breathless; his face had turned cold and grey. Slowly his eyes opened from his deep daze and he watched as the owl landed back on its roost and gawked suspiciously at Carragah, unsure as to what had just happened.

"We need to rest for a while," replied Lepy. "In fact I know just the place," and off he went, leading the way.

After a short distance, a pointed round tower reluctantly divulged its location from the engulfing darkness.

"Wow, a round tower," exclaimed Graham.

"A round tower, is this where they lock up the princess?" Lorna replied innocently.

"No, you dipstick!" Graham replied abruptly.

"Well what do you know?" Lorna snapped back.

"It's where they kept lookout centuries ago for raiding Vikings," Carragah interrupted.

"Isn't it funny all these years later we're using it again," Lepy said, pointing to the old doorway which was at least fifteen feet off the floor. "Well it's not actually funny," he continued, mumbling to himself.

The tower was circular in shape and about a hundred feet tall with a pointed roof similar to the shape of a rocket. Constructed from large ancient stones that appeared grey due to centuries of abrasion from the wind and rain. There were some small arches for windows high in the tower so the lookouts could watch the surrounding countryside for raiders.

From the arched doorway, a rope was dangling down just a foot or two off the ground.

Lepy jumped, managing to grab the rope first time and with the aid of knots every foot or so climbed up into the doorway.

Carragah was last up the rope, clambering to his feet he gazed up into dark empty room where a stone staircase spiralled up. When he stepped off, Lepy pulled the rope up and shut the mature oak door.

"We should be safe up here," Lepy announced and they all collapsed onto the floor.

The four of them sat against the round wall; after a few silent moments they fell asleep. Graham's head drooped forward and his eyelids started dancing emphatically. Seconds later he was walking over the tranquil fields of Knocknakil, the sun was shining and there was enchanting music and laughing coming from beyond the hill. Slowly he walked around the hill to see several leprechauns singing and dancing around an open fire. Glancing around, he noticed numerous small entrances into the hillside where a couple of young female leprechauns came running out. They wore beautiful green dresses and their hair was blonde and tied into braids. Catching Graham's eyes, they giggled and ran off. He realised these were their houses, on top of the mounds the sweet smell of turf escaped through small chimneys and he felt a delightful atmosphere fill the air.

The sound of music increased with small cheers celebrating. He turned in the direction of the noise and noticed a large group of leprechauns moving towards the fire. Instantly, Graham recognised Lepy, he looked younger and was walking with a beautiful female leprechaun. Their arms were linked, she had a stunning green dress on and pink flowers tied into her hair. Graham was flabbergasted with her beauty and noticed them both smiling contently at him, it was their wedding day.

Instantly, Graham was woken by the sound of voices; he looked at his companions, they were all exhausted and had fallen asleep unintentionally. Lepy was staring at Graham in a peculiar way. Suddenly Graham remembered his dream; it was only a dream yet it felt so real. The voices continued. Abruptly, Graham realised there was danger and his attention switched. Graham prodded Lorna, holding his finger over his mouth so they were quiet.

The voices were now at the bottom of the tower and he could hear what they were saying.

"Oi, where are you going, we have got work to do," said a coarse voice with an unusual accent.

"What, walk round on a wild goose chase looking for four people including a leprechaun? We both know it's some big joke."

"No, we have a job to do; we have to capture them for Iroquois dead or alive!" the second voice replied.

Lorna and Graham stared at each other instantly.

"Well he won't know if we have a kip in here will he? Oh no, look there's no ladder. Ah well, the floor it is."

Graham peeked through a small crack in the wooden door. He could see two Viking soldiers both in full body armour and carrying swords and shields.

Graham whispered to Lorna "We're trapped; there is no other way down from here".

"Get up now!" the voice demanded.

"Why, what you going to do about it?"

"It's not me you need to worry about, it's Iroquois; he has been known to rip out peoples' tongues if they fail to follow his instructions."

"Well maybe Iroquois should be worried about me."

"I will let you tell him then," and one of the guards walked off.

"No, no, its OK, I'm coming."

"They're going now," Graham said, pulling away from the door and listening to the voices moving away into the distance.

"Phew, that was a little close for comfort; we'll wait for another half hour and then move to the bottomless lake. If we make it by morning maybe there is at least some chance of survival," Lepy said.

The next few minutes were spent in silence; Graham's thoughts returned to his dream, it felt so real and the way Lepy was staring at him when he woke made him suspicious he knew something about his dream.

Lepy slowly opened the door before dropping the rope down.

"Wait here, whilst I check the coast is clear," he barked, rapidly sliding down the rope.

"Do you think he's OK Graham, he's been gone quite a long time?" Lorna said, looking through the doorway.

"Maybe we should go and look for him?" Graham replied.

"Give him another couple of minutes," Carragah said.

"Right, I'm going looking for him," Graham said a few minutes later and still no sign.

He climbed down the rope into the unknown, beads of perspiration forming on his forehead. Graham edged out of the tower and into the night air; he heard a twig crack on the floor behind him.

Slowly he turned, fearful of seeing the soldiers in his unprotected position.

Lepy appeared from the shadows. "Come on, it's safe to proceed and we can use that dry stone wall to hide our movements against the sky." Graham sighed with relief. Lorna and Carragah climbed down and they started to walk off towards one of the many stone walls littering the land.

Lorna looked skywards, noticing the clear night and the banana-shaped moon.

"Have you seen the stars, Graham?" Lorna whispered.

Graham gazed upwards, the stars in the sky twinkled, unaware of their struggle for survival. This rich and picturesque landscape was now dark, sinister and dangerous. They had been walking for about fifteen minutes around the edge of stone walls when Graham noticed a small fire burning in the direction they were heading.

"Get down," Graham whispered and they all dropped to their hands and knees. Graham let out a small chuckle.

"Lorna, look, Lepy is stood upright but still has less chance of been spotted than us." Lorna chuckled.

"Oh don't be so cheeky!" Lepy replied, flapping his hands downwards in a 'quieten down' gesture as they approached the light.

"It's those Vikings from the tower," Graham said, tapping Lepy lightly on the arm.

"Bang, the little green leprechaun is history!" said one of the soldiers, swiping his sword across, to the amusement of his friend.

Lorna let out a low nervous laugh only to be greeted by serious stern frown from Lepy.

"What, I'm nervous," she whispered in response, shrugging her shoulders.

Edging slowly to the wall they crawled down the side quietly; the two unsavoury characters were directly on the other side. Graham heard them joking about what they would do to the leprechaun to get his gold. No mention was made about Carragah but they did say the kids would wish they had stayed in England after Iroquois was finished.

Edging past, Graham was sure his breathing was so loud that at any time they would jump over and grab him. "That was close," said Lorna "How far have we to go Lepy, it all looks the same to me in the dark?"

"Only another mile or so, let's hope they don't have too many search parties."

"My knees are aching," Graham complained, standing up slowly and it took a few steps before he could walk normally again.

"I'm with you there Graham; I have never walked so far on my hands and knees," Lorna replied.

The countryside was unpredictable; Graham and Lorna found it hard going in the poor light and found themselves frequently tripping up and landing face down.

Luckily, none of them landed in the countless cow pats scattered around. The field dropped into a valley and the cows were lying down chewing as they lay.

Slowly, they turned their heads, watching them pass, uninterested or oblivious to their plight.

The silence was broken with the sound of a dog barking some way behind. "Sounds like they may have dogs picking up our scents," Lepy said, looking worried.

"Let's head west across the river and approach the lake from the other side. Hopefully that will throw them off the scent for a short while, long enough for us to make it to the lake," Carragah suggested.

"Is that someone hiding over there?" Lorna asked, dropping instantly to her knees.

"No it's just a bush," Lepy replied

"The darkness is playing tricks on my eyes; I keep thinking I see something," Lorna continued, climbing back on her feet.

"Yeah, same here," Graham replied.

The glistening moonlight reflecting off the ripples on the river revealed they had arrived at the waterside.

Lorna watched the swift current rushing over the protruding rocks, desperately seeking the safety of the ocean. The sound of the strong surges of water constantly flowing somehow offered her an ounce of comfort.

There was no time to celebrate, they needed to cross this raging torrent and fast, the barks were now getting anxiously louder.

Graham stumbled and fell as he entered the water; his arms hit the rocks below and stopped his torso from a cold wet soaking. The river pushed at his heels and calves, it was no longer inviting it was trying its best to drag him in. Lorna managed to make it across, followed a short time later by Graham. Just as he climbed the bank on the other side he slipped slightly on the mud.

Graham regained his footing and turned to see how the others were progressing. He noticed Carragah carrying Lepy on his back when all of a sudden Carragah lost his footing in the middle of the river. The weight of Lepy must have been just enough to tip the balance; they both landed fully into the water. Lorna ran to the water's edge, the torrent was strong, pulling at her feet.

Carragah fought and successfully managed to climb to his feet.

"Where's Lepy, I can't see any sign of him!" Lorna shouted nervously.

Graham ran down the bank to where Lorna stood. "Where is he?" His heart was sinking.

"Is it possible to survive so long?" Lorna gasped frantically, stamping up the riverside.

Graham gasped, unable to say anything. Frantically he searched the dark glistening water for a hint of where he could be.

"No sign of him, anywhere!" Lorna said with a long a face and her hands on her hips.

Suddenly, Graham noticed the leprechaun's feet protruding and moving quickly in the current away from them. Lepy's boots were kicking frantically, trying to regain composure and flick himself back above the water. Without thinking, Graham jumped in, lurching towards this splashing foot waving in the air. The pace of the river was now torrential, purposely hauling Lepy away. He dived despairingly, hoping to make contact before the leprechaun was washed away. As his face hit the fresh water and dropped below the surface, he lost sight of Lepy's boot still frantically kicking.

Lorna gasped in amazement as Graham disappeared below the surface. Beneath the surface, Graham threw his hand forward hoping to make contact with his small frame. Fortunately, as he clasped his hand, it grabbed Lepy securely. Instantaneously, Graham regained his footing. Lorna watched as he managed to stand holding Lepy up by his foot above the raging river. Dripping, he looked at Graham and smiled. "Thanks Graham!"

They climbed back on the bank where Carragah was waiting.

"Well I'm not asking you to help me across the river again!" shouted Lepy, staring at Carragah.

"Do you know how embarrassing it is been lifted out by your boot, eh?" and he stomped off up the river bank muttering to himself. Carragah looked at Graham and Lorna; they all burst out in fits of laughter, a way of releasing the nervous tension.

The silent night gave way to a whizzing noise that flew above their heads at a frightening speed. A second or two later a crack rang out as a large spear penetrated deeply into the ground just beyond them.

"There they are, get them!" a chilling voice beckoned from the other side of the river.

They glanced back across the river.

"More Vikings!" shouted Lorna nervously.

"Run!" shouted Lepy and they all started running as fast as they could.

"There's the bottomless lake!" Lepy shouted, pointing forwards as he ran.

In the distance, Graham could just start to make out the water's reflection.

"What will we do at the bottomless lake Carragah?" Graham gasped breathlessly, running as hard as he could.

"Like the swallow hole in the stream there is a secret entrance just below the surface."

Graham glanced up at Lorna who was running ahead; she was always a faster runner. Suddenly she disappeared, Graham tried to stop running but his momentum carried him forward like a freight train. Trying frantically to stop, he soon found the reason for Lorna's departure. His stomach ended up in his mouth as he landed heavily on some rocks and stones.

"What is this?" Lorna demanded.

"It's a quarry that was hidden in the darkness. Ouch!" Graham screeched as he felt a heavy bang on his back. Lorna chuckled as she saw Lepy land heavily on her friend's back.

"Thanks Graham, you broke my fall. Why, you are looking after me tonight," Lepy said, quickly looking around to see where the pursuers were.

"They've gone the wrong way," he whispered and dropped back down. Carragah appeared holding his leg.

"Are you OK?" Graham whispered.

"Yes I think so."

Carragah continued: "There's the lake." Graham and Lorna looked across – it was only a hundred yards away.

"Right, once we get there stay with me and I will get us into the concealed entrance in the lake. We will be safe there." The three accomplices nodded. Lepy climbed to the edge of the quarry. "Oh no, they're heading this way."

"Right let's go," ordered Carragah.

"Is that dogs I hear?" Lorna said, with her hand over her ear.

The silent air was broken with the sound of howling dogs.

"I don't think they sound like dogs!" Lepy said, climbing up to the edge of the quarry.

"Wolves! Not seen them in these parts for centuries," he shouted, jumping back in the quarry.

"The howls are getting nearer," Graham shouted, starting to panic.

"Right come on, to the lake," ordered Carragah, rising to his feet and ushering them forward. Quickly they all jumped and started running as fast as their bodies would carry them.

The wolves were virtually on top of them directly, howling and snarling. Graham quickly glanced back, noticing dozens of them foaming and drooling at the mouths.

"There is no way we are going to make it to the lake!" he cried as his legs were starting to give way.

"In there," pointed Carragah with his staff.

The stone circles started to surrender their location in the dark night and they all quickly ran into the centre. Positioning themselves with their backs pushed against each other they peered into the darkness to see if the wolves had noticed.

Just beyond the edge of the erect rocks, the wolves started to appear and snarl. Glancing around the circumference, each gap in the rocks was filled with wolves entering the circle. Cautiously, they started to edge towards them. Lepy raised his sword, took a step forward and struck at the nearest wolf. It let out an awful howl as the sword connected with his snout. The howl penetrated the night air alerting any interested parties of their exact location.

"Leave this to me," Lorna said stepping forward.

"I admire your courage Lorna," Carragah said, pulling her back abruptly by the collar.

In all directions they edged in, fangs protruding, snarling and ready for the kill.

Chapter 14

The Castle at Knocknakil

T HE NEAREST BEAST SNARLED AT LEPY, SNAPPING with its powerful jaws. Lepy's sword flashed in the air and made contact with its snout, pushing him back only to be replaced instantly by another hungry predator. The wolves appeared from all directions, grey dishevelled coats and glorious snarling, white teeth threatening the terrorised party. They closely huddled together in the centre of the circle, their backs tightly pushed against each other desperately fighting off each menacing lunge.

"Lap oh Sact Omono." Carragah appeared in a trance, holding the staff at the glass ball. The wolves were starting to get at Lepy and only the prods from the sword prevented him from being snatched.

The largest wolf snapped at Lorna, she leant backwards kicking at the attacker, suddenly her foot slipped and she fell, landing on her back. The wolf went to bite her leg but only managed to penetrate her jeans. It pulled at her, its jaw locked trying to haul her away from the others. Inch by inch she edged away as it pulled her relentlessly towards the vicious pack.

"Graham, HELP!!!" she screamed.

Graham grabbed her shoulders fighting a tug of war with this brute, preventing the wolf from dragging her off.

A single beam of light quickly intensified around the base of the stone circles.

It accelerated clockwise, rising to the tops of the stones, giving the impression they were inside an extremely fast fairground ride. Carragah lifted his staff high above his head. At its summit, a perfect white light emitted towards the stone circle, intensifying, creating an energy field.

The wolves on the edge of the circle howled as the newly-created energy beam disintegrated everything in its path. Instantly, they violently shattered into crumbling grains of dust which fell harmlessly inside the ancient circle.

The remainder in the circle quickly tried to escape, only to suffer the same fate as the others. One wolf remained, it snapped at Lorna's leg again, narrowly missing her flesh. Determined, it continued to pull and Graham started to lose his grip. "HELP, STOP IT GRAHAM!" Lorna screamed.

The energy field crept in towards the centre of the circle; inch by inch it swallowed the remaining wolf. Just as it reached its head it howled and instantly exploded into ash and Lorna was free.

The still night air was filled with the cries of the condemned animals and the stench of burning flesh. As the last wolf befell its fate, the light disbanded and Carragah fell heavily onto his knees.

Lorna leapt to her feet and embraced Graham tightly; no words were needed.

A sudden gust of cold wind blew across the plains.

"We must get to the lake," whispered Carragah, breathless and struggling to climb to his feet following the ritual. Lepy looked at Carragah, his face full of concern; he had never seen him looking so weak.

Jumping to their feet, they started towards the lake.

"There they are!" shouted an unfamiliar voice from behind.

Graham's heart was pounding out of his chest. The four of them were tired and worn out and running again but their momentum was declining. The ground became softer with large rushes protruding from the spongy ground causing Lepy to struggle with the terrain.

Seconds later he fell into a spiky rush, exhausted and unable to continue his flight, accepting his fate he lay lifeless on the floor.

"Lepy," Lorna shouted, quickly stopping.

"Go, leave me, I will be fine, I would rather perish than be carried by a girl," Lepy shouted, defeated.

"No chance!" shouted Lorna, determination shining through the serious frown; she grabbed Lepy, much to his disapproval, and tucked him under her right arm.

Sprinting resolutely she quickly caught up; after what felt like days they arrived at the lake. Graham let out a sigh of relief as they started to slow and the heavy breathing and voices of their pursuers sounded some distance away.

A deep familiar serrated voice destroyed the moment.

"Going somewhere Carragah?"

As they approached the lake, a dark image emerged from the shadows standing directly in their way. A large man; his long dark coat flapping as he moved forward, his heavy boots submerging deep into the soft ground.

"Iroquois," Carragah sighed heavily, disappointed and shattered.

"Who else would you be expecting?"

Lorna pulled at Graham's arm and nodded backwards with her head intent on escape.

Iroquois shouted, "Gregorian".

As Graham and Lorna discreetly turned around, several large Vikings greeted them, blocking any escape route.

Iroquois let out an awful laugh which sent chills down Graham's spine and he shivered uncontrollably. His long menacing sword somehow managed to catch the moonlight as the fiend waved it provocatively.

"I think you will find there is no escape this time." The soldiers quickly moved in and grabbed the four of them from behind, tightly restraining their hands.

Graham and Lorna instantly started to struggle; however the more they struggled the more the pressure increased on their wrists. Lorna stopped her resistance as she felt her wrist about to break, closely followed by Graham.

"Get off me!" Lepy screamed, tightly tucked under a soldier's arm. He was kicking and screaming but this soldier was disciplined with a tight clench.

"Bring them," Iroquois ordered and he started leading the way away from the safety of the lake.

Silently they were marched up the lane directly past Aunt's farmhouse. Without thinking Graham shouted "Aunt!" trying to raise the alarm.

His head violently surged forward, feeling as if it was about to come off his shoulders, as the guard smacked him viciously. Graham's ears were left with a high pitch noise as he realised what had happened. Glancing back towards the farmhouse, Graham started to lose hope, comprehending there were no signs of life.

At the bottom of the lane, Iroquois opened a gate and soldiers forced them all through with little resistance. Progressing through the field, the lifeless cows sat there chewing, watching them pass as if this was a daily occurrence. The field gradually became steeper, changing into a sharp hill.

With firm and consistent force, Graham steadily progressed up the mound, where he noticed a large structure set against the dark sky.

"Can you see that up there Lorna?" Graham asked as the guard gave him an abrupt push forward.

"Yeah, it looks like an old castle," she replied.

"Never heard about this place," Graham continued, receiving another unwanted push.

The castle haunted the skyline; there were several large dark windows lifeless and uninviting. The large defensive walls had decayed over time just like the abbeys a mile or so down the road. Approaching the dark shadowy construction, the parties were forced through an archway door. There was a metal gate just visible high in the arch of the door, it was heavily corroded. Lorna noticed the walls, extremely thick and made from rock; it had thin slants like windows, particularly around the entrance.

"Jim never mentioned this place, he must have known about it," Graham said to Lorna.

"I wouldn't blame him for not mentioning it; this place gives me the creeps," Lorna replied.

It was sinister inside, circular in shape and the walls appeared to close in. Although they had disintegrated over time, they were too high to climb over.

Iroquois walked to the centre of the forecourt, which was about the size of a tennis court. The guards forced the prisoners to the centre and kicked them at the back of the knees until they fell in the kneeling position.

One of the guards got some torches and set fire to them. He then placed a few around the castle walls, increasing the light and sordid atmosphere.

"Come here Carragah!" Iroquois demanded, pointing to the floor in front of him. Carragah ignored his demand.

The two men behind quickly grabbed him and threw him on the floor in front of Iroquois.

"Give me the key to the burial chambers," demanded Iroquois.

Carragah kept his head bowed without comment.

"What key?" whispered Lorna.

"I don't know," Graham replied, receiving another stiff blow to the back of his head. Graham quickly looked round at the guard dishing out the punishment, who was smiling, enjoying his sadistic reprimands. The guard continued pointing at Graham and pulling his finger across his neck indicating he was going to slit his throat.

"The key, Carragah!" Iroquois shouted. Still there was no reply.

Taking a step backwards, Iroquois struck him hard across the head. Carragah collapsed on the floor. He then took hold of Carragah throwing him around like a rag doll. Reaching inside his cloak he pulled out the old Celtic cross used at the stone circles. Iroquois held his precious treasure aloft, resembling a winning captain lifting the trophy.

"Ah, that's the key!" exclaimed Graham, realising its significance.

Instantly, he received another stiff smack from behind which left him with a whistling noise in his ears.

Glancing around, the guard was looking rather pleased with himself.

Graham decided to keep his curses silent along with his thoughts of retribution.

"Gregorian, throw them in the dungeons until I decide their fate," Iroquois ordered.

Gregorian nodded his head and the guards abruptly seized the prisoners.

"Remember to leave someone guarding them; the Boggot will want to see Carragah alive, at least for now." Gregorian nodded.

"Oh Gregorian, one more thing, the boy was shouting for his Aunt back near the farmhouse, it might be a good idea to send someone round to look after her."

"Yes, Iroquois," Gregorian replied, quickly looking at the nearest guard.

"Raven, get round to the farmhouse and look after her." The nearest guard nodded his head as he started to move away.

"No, leave her alone!" Graham shouted defiantly.

Guthrum unleashed another harsh clout across the back of Graham's head, which instantly silenced him.

"Don't worry Graham, the guard will wish he had stayed here," Carragah said reassuringly.

Graham smiled, trying to keep his hopes up.

The guards quickly hustled them through the forecourt into a dark arched doorway and down a spiral stone staircase leading to a long dark corridor. Towards the end of the passageway, Graham noticed a small arch at floor level, more like a window than a door. As they approached, he could see a rusted metal door with a large old-fashioned padlock on.

Gregorian bent down and unlocked the padlock, instantly the remaining guards threw Carragah through it, quickly followed by the other prisoners.

They all fell heavily on the stone floor of the cell which was below ground level and Gregorian locked the padlock.

"I will guard them!" the sadistic guard barked.

"Very well Guthrum, do not harm them!" Gregorian ordered, leading the remaining guards away.

The dungeon was claustrophobic with damp walls and one way out.

"Carragah, what is going to happen to the guard who has gone to get Aunt?"

"Ah, I need to consult with a few friends who will be able to assist," Carragah replied, still very optimistic, much to Graham's approval.

"It's that guard Graham!" said Lorna glancing up a few feet through the metal gate.

"Bloody hell!" Graham gasped, his heart sinking rapidly, catching the eye of Guthrum who was menacingly playing with a small dagger.

"Now what do we do?" said Graham panicking with the thought of the guard above.

"Now then, let me deal with the guard on his way to Knocknakil," Carragah replied, as he sat on the cold floor holding the top of his staff.

Their eyes slowly started to adjust in the dark cell and they could now see each other. Carragah was deep in thought, his eyes tightly closed, quietly he whispered into the dense atmosphere.

"We have got to escape," Lorna said, feeling along the solid stone walls.

The gate rattled and they quickly looked up and noticed Guthrum unlocking the padlock and suspiciously glancing backwards. After releasing the lock he opened the gate "Right you lot, who's first?" he whispered sadistically holding his dagger in their direction.

"What about you, Graham?" he continued.

Graham was anxious and quickly edged back to the furthest point of the cell as Guthrum dropped into the cell.

"Where are you Guthrum?" a voice echoed down the passageway.

Quickly he placed his dagger back in his belt and turned to climb back out.

Lepy ran towards him and the guard kicked out sending the leprechaun sprawling.

"What are you doing in there, Gregorian will be very angry," he said, helping Guthrum out.

"Here are some refreshments," he continued, handing Guthrum a jug of wine. Instantly he drank from it and the wine flowed down his gullet loudly. The other guard relocked the padlock and disappeared again.

Guthrum sat back on a chair and stared in. "Don't worry Graham, you will wait." His chilling laugh filled the air and he took another enormous gulp.

"I'm dead!" Graham whispered, shaking his head and staring at the floor.

"Not if I have anything to do with it!" Lepy whispered, revealing the guard's dagger.

Edging down the steep-sided valley, Iroquois and Gregorian merged into the surroundings assisted by the heavy mist. They slowly approached the long-forgotten dilapidated cottage carefully, navigating the sharp rocks. A long creak echoed through the sleepy valley as Iroquois opened the door. Walking through the sparse room they went down the stairs deep into the ground. A fire was in full flow, hissing and snapping at the approaching intruders.

"Iroquois, you have something for me?" a voice in the shadows asked.

"Yes, I have brought the key to the secret burial grounds," he replied respectfully.

"Come bring it to me," he ordered, remaining concealed in the shadows.

Iroquois edged forward and held out his arm with the cross tightly clenched in his hand.

"Ah, Iroquois you don't know how long I have waited for this moment." A long wrinkly hand with long dirty nails appeared from the shadows, it lightly touched the cross still embedded in Iroquois' hand.

"You have performed well," he continued, retracting his hand back into the shadows.

"Now take this and place it in the stone circle at sunrise and the entrance will emerge, Gregorian."

"Yes, sire," he replied, stepping forward and trying to peer through the shadows to see his master.

"Where are your men?"

"They are guarding the prisoners."

"Good, make sure they don't touch anything in the chambers and keep that Carragah in your sights at all times, looks can be deceiving."

"Yes sire," he replied, stepping backwards.

"Now go and complete your task. Be wary, Carragah will not give up the burial chambers without a fight."

"What do you want me to do with the old man and the children?" inquired Iroquois.

"When we have access to the chambers and spring, they are dispensable, but make sure no one ever finds the remains."

"With pleasure," Iroquois replied and they left the isolated cottage.

Chapter 15

On a Knife's Edge

THE JUG COLLAPSED ON THE STONE FLOOR, catapulting shards of sharp pottery in all directions. Four sets of eyes gazed intently from a forgotten piece of Ireland. Guthrum's head dropped, instantly jolting upright as he fought the urge to sleep. The battle-hardened soldier in full body armour was slumped against the wall, struggling to get comfortable on the stone floor. Throwing his helmet down, it bounced, spinning around, its horns landing facing through the metal gate. Lorna noticed the guard's matted light hair which had not seen water for generations. Seconds later he was snoring, much to the relief of Graham.

"Lorna, give me a lift up to the gate," said Lepy, holding the guard's dagger.

Bending down on her knees, Lepy climbed up onto her shoulders. Slowly Lorna clambered to her feet and Lepy leant carefully through the gaps in the gate. He withdrew the knife and started to pick at the steel lock, peering every few seconds at the guard.

Approaching the farm house from the dark deserted country lane the figure of a large man slowly climbed over a dry stone wall. Hiding behind the broad trunks of several large ash trees, the Viking warrior cautiously inched forward, intent on keeping the element of surprise. Experience had taught him that victims don't struggle as much when they are not aware he is going to slash their throats. Callously, he withdrew his sharp lacerated dagger, noticing Kathleen at the kitchen window. Raven looked skywards into the dark night; the trees suddenly came to life, their branches becoming

114

animated. Whispers filled the air as the trees spoke to each other. Raven started to feel uneasy, the branches swayed deliberately but there was no wind. He shook his head, trying to concentrate on the task at hand and inched forward. After a couple more steps a branch clipped his shoulder quickly followed by another. A deep eerie feeling overcame Raven, beads of perspiration appearing on his forehead, his heart started beating so loudly he could hear it. Grasping his sword, he hacked at the nearest branch. It let out a small cry which unnerved the guard further, he was now utterly frightened. Another branch moved towards his leg, instantly he lifted his sword above his head to strike at it. Instinctively Raven's body posture changed as he pulled the sword down to bear. Unexpectedly, the sword jerked from his hand; impulsively looking back, he saw a twig wrapped around it, lifting the weapon high out of his reach. Abruptly, he turned as several branches wrapped around his legs pulling him off his feet. Frantically he tried to crawl away but more and more branches engulfed him, now pulling him across the ground effortlessly. He screamed as the roots of the nearest tree heaved him down towards the earth, slowly the soft ground started to engulf him, only his head remained in view. As he let out his last futile scream, the soil crept above his face muffling his cry and condemning him to the land. Calm quickly returned and the whispering stopped; no traces remained of the warrior.

Seconds later, Carragah snapped out of his trance.

"You don't need to worry about that guard anymore, your Aunt is safe," Carragah said, looking totally worn out and exhausted.

"Why what happened?" Graham asked, feeling relieved.

"I will explain it to you when all this is over."

"What will happen now Iroquois has the key?" Graham whispered to Carragah, conscious not to wake the guard.

"Well, Graham, I'm not sure. However, you and Lorna will have your part to play," he replied, placing his hand on Graham's shoulders.

"What do you mean?"

"It is no coincidence that you are here, Graham."

"I'm just on my holiday, or I was," he replied, looking confused.

"Graham, these are desperate times. If Iroquois gains entry to the chambers and the spring, he will have access to a boundless energy source that not only supplies the Earth's energy fields, it ensures life survives as we know it. Unfortunately, it can also guarantee his eternity along with others."

"You mean the spring can grant eternal life?"

"Whoever controls this natural spring, can do anything."

"Oi! What you doing?" Guthrum shouted, kicking the gate and Lepy with it.

The leprechaun flew backwards and the knife dropped on to the floor near the guard's foot. Guthrum stared into the cell waking from his sleep. Lepy's momentum flung the pair of them into the corner of the cell, landing in a tangled heap. Lorna took the full force of the fall and was lying holding her lower back from the impact.

"Bloody hell," she exclaimed, disappointed and sore, climbing to her knees.

They all fell silent and looked at the guard hoping the urge to sleep would return and get the better of him.

"If he sees the knife, we're in big trouble," Lorna whispered, staring at it, inches from Guthrum's foot. As the guard adjusted his position, he knocked the knife slightly with his foot which clinked on the hard floor.

Lorna's heart skipped a beat expecting the guard to notice it any second. He peered into the cell until he made eye contact with Graham then repeated his threat with his finger across his throat.

The standoff ensued for several minutes until Guthrum started to nod again. Moving his body he caught the knife with his foot sending it flying into the metal gate with a large bang before it dropped harmlessly next to Lepy's foot. Guthrum jumped up on hearing the bang, he looked at the padlock and then the four prisoners. Searching the floor around his body and passageway for several minutes, he noticed small fragments of pottery. However, he was quiet satisfied all was in order. He lay down, staring in again, paying particular attention to Graham.

After a silent few minutes, Guthrum's head dropped and he was asleep. Lepy whispered to Lorna and they both stood up. Lepy climbed on his shoulders and started to work on the lock.

"Careful, Lepy!" Graham gasped as the gate banged. The guard did not move, he was soundly asleep.

"Yes!" Lepy roared as the lock fell heavily to the floor with an unmistakable thud that echoed throughout the hushed corridor and the County of Mayo.

The atmosphere was extremely tense; perspiration fell heavily from the old grey-haired druid. Jerking, the guard lifted his head to see what had made the noise.

"Not again!" Lorna exclaimed, realising their time was up.

Miraculously, Guthrum's chin drooped onto his chest as he snored and fell back to sleep.

Instantly, Lorna lifted Lepy through the gate, who in turn assisted the rest of the party to climb up. Graham picked up the padlock and quietly dropped the soldier's helmet into the cell before locking the gate in an act of defiance. Guthrum snorted a few times but within seconds they were sneaking up the passage to freedom. Lepy lead the way and peeked through the door to see if the coast was clear. Just beyond the arched doorway sat another guard, soundly asleep. Lepy beckoned them forward and they slowly crept into the forecourt and past the guard. Travelling in the shadows next to the wall, Graham noticed a small gap in the wall just large enough to squeeze through.

Lorna instantly dropped to her feet and crawled through and out of sight. A few seconds later she reappeared. "Come on we can get out this way!" she said and disappeared again. They all crawled through and out into the shadows of a gloomy open field.

"Right, we must get to the Secret Burial Ground; I think the time has come to call on the protectors of Knocknakil," Carragah said, leaning heavily on his staff.

"The protectors, who are they!" Lorna interrupted abruptly.

"Can it be done? I heard old tales but never thought it was true," Lepy replied, looking confused.

"Hello, protectors, who are they?" Lorna interrupted sarcastically.

"You know those four tombs in the chambers?" Lepy replied.

"Well yes, you don't mean...?" Lorna gasped.

"That's right, calling the knights sworn to protect the grounds for all time," Lepy continued.

"Get down!" Graham whispered, collapsing to the ground quickly.

They all followed suit, silently falling to earth.

Iroquois and Gregorian stomped past without noticing four artificial bumps only a few feet away and into the castle entrance.

As soon as they disappeared into the castle, Lepy directed them back towards the stone circle.

Entering the forecourt, Iroquois looked up towards the dark night sky. Just towards the east, the sky was slightly lighter, hinting that sunrise was imminent.

"Ah, the time is quickly approaching. Come, let's get Carragah," said Iroquois, heading over the forecourt, quickly followed by Gregorian.

They approached the guard at the forecourt entrance to the dungeons, who quickly scrambled to his feet after hearing the voices and the encroaching heavy steps.

"Everything been OK?" enquired Gregorian, not noticing the drowsy soldier had only just woken.

"Yes, nothing to report," he replied standing with his chest out.

Iroquois stared right through him as he ducked to enter through the low arched doorway into the prison passageway.

As they progressed down the walkway, they noticed Guthrum lying flat on the stone floor snoring.

"What's this, Gregorian?" he raged, moving quickly towards the lethargic guard and giving him a firm kick.

"Guthrum!" Gregorian shouted as the guard scrambled to his feet wearily.

"S... s... sorry, I don't know what happened!" the apologetic guard replied.

"Open the gate!" ordered Iroquois, unable to see in from his location.

Scrambling for his keys, Guthrum moved towards the padlock and started to unlock it. His eyes gazed through the gap and he realised the cell was empty. Guthrum froze and his eyes instantly gave him away. Iroquois threw him out of the way and peered in at the cold stone walls.

Instantly flying into a rage, Iroquois drew his sword and lifted to slay Guthrum.

"Stop Iroquois, he is my best soldier!" shouted Gregorian, pleading with him to spare the slothful fool.

Regaining control, Iroquois re-sheathed his sword. "Guthrum, this is only a reprieve. If we don't find them, I will finish the job!" and he turned away, ordering Gregorian to follow.

"You never know, Iroquois, I might finish you off," sneered the disgruntled guard, making sure his voice was too low to be heard.

Chapter 16

Protectors

WHERE THE SPARKLING OCEAN UNITES WITH THE light blue sky, a few unspoilt rays of dazzling sunlight entered the horizon. A blackbird sung in high spirits, abruptly ending its infectious melody, noticing the encroaching danger. The stone circles stood proudly as they had done for thousands of years. Even they seemed to somehow disapprove of the arrival of the gloomy band as they drew near.

Stopping a short distance away, Iroquois scoured the surroundings looking for a hint of Carragah. He looked at the stone circle where the entrance to the burial grounds had appeared. The surroundings were quiet and unspoilt, nobody around to prevent Iroquois and his band from finally gaining access to the tombs.

The sun reluctantly stirred, intuitively sensing the land's discontent but unable to prevent its own progress.

"Gregorian, I trust your men won't let us down again?"

"No, they are in position, any unwanted visitors will be advised to come back later," he started to smile.

Iroquois did not share the joke and with a face of thunder he moved towards the stone circle. "Just make sure they don't Gregorian, next time it will be you who will take responsibility."

Gregorian chose not to reply and just shook his head. Looking round, he could see his soldiers positioned strategically, with Guthrum furthest away.

Iroquois moved to the largest rock and placed the Celtic cross inside the recess of the rock. The sun slowly ascended and the rays of light were now escaping freely. Iroquois stood backwards and watched the sun creep skywards.

Sun rays quickly glided over glimmering dew-covered fields before finally arriving at the stone circle. Rapidly they shone on the stones, including the largest with the key inset into it.

"Nothing is happening!" Iroquois shouted impatiently, looking at Gregorian.

Seconds later, the rocks started to shake and the earth moved as the two great posts slowly ascended skywards revealing the secret entrance.

A small dust cloud formed, concealing the opening for a few seconds. As it cleared, Iroquois moved forward to the unprotected entrance and gawped inside. Slowly, he took a step forward and started to move inside; suddenly a flash of light caught his hand, pushing it away ferociously, leaving it numb and listless. Illuminated against the dark passageway, Iroquois noticed a hazy dust-filled light protecting the entrance; a gentle electrical buzz confirmed the field remained as the haze faded.

"Carragah!!" he screamed and stepped back out of the doorway beckoning Gregorian.

"What's happening?" Gregorian asked, responding to Iroquois' call.

"There is some energy field protecting the way in."

"Energy field," Gregorian replied, totally confused.

"It some old druid spell, he must be close. Get your men and find him now, he must be around here somewhere!" Iroquois ordered.

Gregorian sounded a horn and his men quickly arrived from all directions.

"Carragah is close at hand and is protecting the way in. We must find him now."

They dispersed into small groups and scoured the surrounding area. Just past the stone circles, Guthrum noticed a small quarry hidden in the field. He prompted his accomplice to go into the quarry first. As he peered down from above, he noticed Carragah alone with his stick embedded into the floor. He was in a trance, whispering. The guard grabbed the stick instantly, breaking the seal on the entrance to the chamber. Suddenly a rock struck the guard's helmet and he fell heavily. Lorna and Graham swiftly came into view, throwing more heavy rocks at the disabled soldier. Then the leprechaun jumped into the fray with his miniature sword. The soldier began to regain his composure and started to climb to his feet, drawing his sword. Lepy thrust his sword forward, moving him dangerously close to the soldier. His thrust hit the target and into the soft underbelly of the towering man. The soldier gasped breathlessly; rapidly he looked skywards as light shone out of his stomach where the wound was. In seconds, the bright light had completely enveloped his whole body. As quickly as the light appeared, it had vanished and with it the soldier.

"Aargh," Guthrum screamed as he dropped into the quarry with his sword drawn.

He swiped viciously at Lepy who lifted his sword in defence. Lepy's sword took the full impact and catapulted out of his hands, embedding deep into the quarry wall.

Guthrum lifted his sword high and swiftly brought it down to bear on the defenceless leprechaun with venom. In a flash, the sword hit something solid and not the soft flesh as he expected.

Instantly, Guthrum noticed Gregorian standing there holding his sword just above the leprechaun, preventing him from harm.

"Iroquois wants them unharmed!" Gregorian said calmly, staring into Guthrum's eyes.

Guthrum didn't reply, his face started to twitch near an old battle scar.

"That was close," said Lorna.

"Tell me about it!!" said Lepy as Guthrum threw him out of the quarry, quickly followed by Lorna and Graham. He then grabbed Carragah and marched him out roughly.

The other soldiers grabbed them tightly. Guthrum, still seething, looked menacingly at the leprechaun. "Next time there will be no one to save you!"

The soldiers marched them to Iroquois who was still near the entrance.

"Carragah, still you continue this futile effort to protect the burial grounds. You must accept your time is over. I will let you live long enough to watch me dip my hand in the fountain of power."

"You will never make it, these sacred grounds are protected," Carragah replied defiantly.

Iroquois laughed. "Old tales, my friend, old tales. Gregorian, grab that girl!" he ordered. Gregorian grabbed Lorna by the arms and led her forward towards the entrance. "Get off me now!" Lorna struggled. Gregorian drew his sword and pushed it into the small of Lorna's back and the struggle stopped.

"Let's hope there are no traps for the girl's sake," Iroquois said as Gregorian pushed the sword into Lorna's back, forcing her forward in through the arched doorway. Slowly he moved deep into the chamber where it split into three chambers.

The Viking soldiers noticed the inscriptions above the door and became agitated.

Iroquois, observing this, said: "Don't worry about these old inscriptions, these are the protectors of the grounds, three children an old man."

"You are a fool, none of you will see the sunset," said Carragah, defiantly.

"Guthrum, check inside that chamber there!" Gregorian ordered.

"You check in that one," he said pointing to another guard.

The two soldiers followed their orders and cautiously moved into the dark chambers, grabbing a torch each from the other guards.

The dancing fire from Guthrum's flame started to reveal some of the hidden treasures. His eyes lit up as he noticed the gold and jewels piled up within the chests. Quickly, he glanced behind to check if anybody had followed. Noticing he was alone, he grabbed some of the jewels in the nearest chest and placed them deep into his clothing. Returning out of the chamber, Guthrum passed an eye-shaped plaque on the wall; it had a small black bulb in its centre. Just as he arrived back to the others, the chamber started to shake, small rocks fell from the ceiling and dust filled the air.

"What did you do in there?" Gregorian demanded, looking at Guthrum.

"Nothing," he replied suspiciously.

Gregorian reached inside Guthrum's cloak and pulled out some gold coins.

"Nothing you fool!" Gregorian shouted as the chamber stopped shaking.

"You are sealed in here for all eternity and have woken those who should not be woken," Carragah said, looking at Iroquois.

Gregorian urgently moved up the passage and noticed the entrance blocked by a solid stone wall.

Returning to Iroquois, no words were spoken, he already knew. "Come, we don't have time for this." And he grabbed Lorna and led her down to the last steep chamber.

The guards nervously looked over their shoulders, a breeze started to flow through the passages and the cobwebs swayed from side to side.

Suddenly a chilling scream echoed from the second chamber where the guard had entered.

"What's that?" Graham gasped, panicking and moving as close to Carragah as possible.

"They have woken,"

"Who has?"

"Those chosen to protect this place," Carragah replied.

"Move in there," Iroquois grunted, pushing Lorna into the last chamber and down the flights of stone stairs.

"There's nothing here, only old burial chambers," Guthrum barked, looking around the lifeless dark cavern.

"Don't be misled, it's here somewhere," Iroquois replied, moving down towards the bridge. Silently looking down into the abyss they walked over the narrow link. Lorna looked forward, trying to keep her mind blank so the realisation of her situation was manageable.

"Light those torches!" Iroquois ordered. A guard ran across towards the arches, hesitating for a few seconds at the sight of the coffins just inside. Flickering, the dim light slowly intensified as the fire on the torches grew more aggressive and the cavern started to divulge some of its concealed underground arches.

The remaining guards released the hostages, spread out across the platform and drew their swords. Inch by inch they moved forward, stopping every few seconds to check behind. Lorna passed the indentations on the ground.

"Look Graham, the coffins," Lorna yelled, pointing enthusiastically in their direction. The stone slabs had somehow been lifted off and placed at the side of each grave.

"Wow, they're empty," he replied, as his hairs on the back of his neck stood proudly, sending cold shivers through his entire body.

The Secret Burial Grounds of Knocknakil

Iroquois noticed the magnificent pool as he passed over the open stone tombs and released Lorna from his strong grasp, moving slowly towards it.

He stopped in his tracks, the sound of metal clanging filled the air, and from the sides of the cavern the protectors appeared.

Chapter 17

The Spring

RAGING RIVERS CARVED THE HONEYCOMBED SHAPED CAVERNS thousands of years ago. The soft limestone eroded by strong rapids, relentlessly flowing beneath the surface, creating history for generations to discover. From where Graham stood it looked as though these caverns stretched for miles. For a few seconds, he admired the beauty and numerous caves and passages that littered this undiscovered terrain. Graham promised himself if he survived this strange and treacherous time he would visit again.

Gregorian, Guthrum and the remaining four guards joined Iroquois past the empty coffins.

"What the bloody hell is that?" Lorna exclaimed.

"I don't know but it looks bad," Graham replied.

Out of a large dark cavern, a shape with a round, brightly covered shield came into view. It had an eye-shaped symbol in the centre.

The shape stood tall and the guard nearest lifted his torch quickly to improve his view, seconds later taking a step backwards in horror.

Under the bronze helmet, two cheek plates came across, covering the majority of the face. The protector looked upwards, revealing an eyeless skull, dark and haunting. Its torso was covered in battle dress tunic which dropped to its knees. Over its clothes, squeaking steel plates joined on to its breast plate which reached just above the waist.

Banging its sword against the shield, it stepped forward, its bones creaking with every step. Seconds later another protector revealed itself from the opposite side of the cavern, quickly followed by another scraping carcass. All of a sudden they stopped without warning and stood to attention, all carrying the same shields. A ghostly glow shrouded their frame, revealing their flesh and faces, before fading again.

"Lorna, they look like that ghost we saw in the passageway!" Graham uttered, moving further away, stuck between whatever these protectors were and Iroquois' men.

"Th... th... they're dead people!" Lorna whispered, horrified, desperately trying not to draw attention to herself.

"That's what you will look like in a thousand years time," Carragah replied, trying to ease the tension, but Lorna was too shocked to respond.

Just near the spring another image appeared; like the others its features were that of a skeleton with a transparent glow. It wore a green tunic with gold embroidered patterns which dropped to its knees. A silver band around its neck supported a long purple cloak which flowed down the length of its back. Around its waist area hung a belt with armour attached which drooped half way down its thigh. The only other protection it possessed were its knee-length metal boots and a rectangular shield which bent around its frame with the same symbol as the others.

Graham looked at his sword. "It's that one off the coffins with the gold handle."

"I can see that, so how does it help?" Lorna snapped back.

"Well, I don't know."

"So why are you telling me?"

Graham decided not to pursue the matter any further.

"Guthrum," ordered Gregorian, nodding his head in the direction of the first protector.

Guthrum nodded in return, drew his sword and held aloft his shield. Slowly he edged out in its direction.

The new protector with the cloak spoke in an ancient language. Instantly, the nearest protector banged his sword against his shield and slowly stepped towards Guthrum. Step by step they moved closer to each other, sparring.

"Who do you think will win Graham?" Lorna asked.

"Don't know if it will matter!" Graham replied, watching the ensuing fight nervously.

CLASH. Guthrum thrusted his sword at the protector, crashing against his shield.

The protector in return launched its attack, hitting Guthrum's sword. Violently they threw their swords at each other with all their might. After a few clashes, the protector lost strength, the glow around its body started to flicker and fade. Noticing the deterioration, Guthrum's confidence grew, with a tremendous blow he knocked the defender to its knees. Sniffing victory, his momentum grew, thrashing again violently as he gained strength. The protector's sword fell and Guthrum's next crash snapped its shield.

Lifting his sword high in the air he screamed as he drove into the defenceless skeleton. Instantly, the protector evaporated into a ball of dust and nothing remained.

Guthrum turned to Gregorian and lifted his sword in victory.

"We're in trouble now!" Graham sighed heavily.

"Should we make a run for it?" Lorna replied in desperation.

"Yeah, if you know a way out?"

The protector near the spring spoke again in his foreign tongue.

Instantly, Carragah replied and a conversation ensued. Iroquois interrupted. "Gregorian, lead your men into final victory. Time has made these protectors weak and they are no match for disciplined soldiers such as you."

Gregorian acknowledged the order and stepped forward, closely followed by his men.

Carragah placed his hand on the top of his staff and released the glass ball that was still glowing since he had dipped it into the spring.

Gregorian's men stepped towards the motionless protectors.

Carragah threw the crystal ball with all his might at the stone floor and it smashed into tiny pieces, releasing a small flash of light that flew high into the air.

"What's that?" Lorna gasped, watching the glorious white comet-shaped light zoom around the room erratically.

Graham shouted as he ducked, narrowly managing to prevent a collision as it flew inches above his head before hovering at the top of the cavern.

"Look Graham!" Lorna shouted, pointing at the protector who had been speaking.

Graham glanced across as the protector lifted his faceless skull skywards and shouted.

The light shot into his rib gage and exploded, dazzling all in the cavern. Graham lifted his arms to protect his eyes from the intense light and fell to his knees. The brightness started to fade and Graham noticed Iroquois, Gregorian and their guards lying on the floor.

"Fantastic," Lorna whispered.

"What?" Graham replied, quickly turning around.

"Oh, my." He was flabbergasted to see the protector was now flesh and bones. Immediately, he noticed his short curly blonde hair and well-defined body. Striking blue eyes stared at the children and he smiled. Immediately they knew that the protectors meant them no harm, if only they could defeat Iroquois and his men. Lifting his sword, which was glowing brightly into the air, he pointed at the two remaining skeletal figures in turn. Flash, lightning bolts shot from the magical sword, creating two more human guardians. Lorna watched as one of them turned his hands over in disbelief.

"Gregorian, attack now before they gain more strength," Iroquois demanded.

A battle cry echoed throughout the cavern as the Vikings went on the offensive.

Lorna grabbed Graham, linking with him, unable to look away. Their future depended on the outcome. Every time swords or shields crashed, Lorna flinched, driving her sharp nails into Graham's arms

Carragah came across and grabbed both their shoulders trying to reassure them. "That is Cuchulain, he won't let us down."

A protector energetically spun round in the air and his sword avoided the Viking's shield and sword, driving deep into his chest. The felled Viking fell to his knees.

From his wound a white light developed; the Viking started to vanish as the light enveloped him. Seconds later, he had gone and the white light concentrated into a ball and flew into the spring. Gradually a potent odour slowly infected the air with a hint of burning flesh.

The protectors and Vikings violently battled against each other. Crash! Another Viking fell, closely followed by another. Each time light escaped from their wounds before completely devouring their bodies and catapulting into the lava.

After several minutes only two Vikings remained, Guthrum and Gregorian, with the two protectors.

"Please come on," Graham gasped, hoping with all his might. The Vikings relentlessly pounded the protectors. Lorna didn't reply, clutching and flinching with every crash of metal on metal. Seconds later and simultaneously, they slayed the remaining two guardians. As they fell, one struck out, catching the unsuspecting Guthrum.

Guthrum fell to his knees, his face twitched and he let out an almighty scream as the light engulfed his body. He valiantly fought the brightness but his fight was futile and seconds later he suffered the same fate.

Gregorian fell to his knees, distraught at the loss of his closest friend.

"AHHH!!!" he screamed as he lost his temper and climbed to his feet. He threw his shield across the ground and sprinted at Cuchulain to exert revenge, twisting his sword as he drew closer.

"No Gregorian!" Iroquois ordered firmly.

It was too late. Gregorian was upon the blonde-haired giant raising his sword to attack. Cleverly, Cuchulain sidestepped the raging Viking and exerted his own justice. His large muscled arms thrust his glowing sword down across the back of Gregorian's shoulder and neck.

Silently, Gregorian realised his mistake and fell onto his knees; he gasped as the brightness started to swallow up his body. Holding out his hand the light pierced through in several places. Glaring skywards his mouth opened wide and the glow shone through, high into the sky like a beacon. Abruptly it burst towards the spring as his time finished, leaving a smouldering stench lingering. Holding their breath, Graham and Lorna valiantly struggled to prevent the odour offending their sense of smell.

The blonde-haired giant smiled at Carragah and moved towards Iroquois.

Iroquois rose to the challenge. "I will just have to finish the job myself."

Cuchulain and Iroquois met and circled each other dangerously close to the brightly coloured spring. The dark honeycomb chambers of the cavern scrutinised the events as whispers soared through the Earth's core informing the unseen of the unfolding proceedings. CRASH! Their swords sparked with the severe force of the impact as they struck at each other with intense force. Suddenly, Iroquois jumped and kicked Cuchulain, his heavy boot connecting firmly on his chest sending him crashing heavily on the floor, losing his sword. Iroquois thrust to take advantage and swung violently at the defenceless guardian. Cuchulain rolled to the side, reaching his sword as Iroquois' sword crashed heavily, sparking against the stone floor. He climbed to his feet and they clashed again. Iroquois moved around the cavern and grabbed a rock and hurled it at Cuchulain, just narrowly missing his unprotected head. As he ducked, Iroquois kicked out sending him crashing yet again.

"This doesn't look good," Graham said shaking his head in despair.

"Come on Cuchulain!" Lorna screamed.

Iroquois thrust his sword, glancing against Cuchulain's unprotected chest. Blood started to seep onto his green clothing. Cuchulain placed his hand on his chest and noticed blood oozing out, he was starting to struggle and Iroquois was relentless, crashing down heavily with every blow of his sword. Suddenly, one of his strong blows caught the protector's sword, sending it crashing several feet away. Iroquois stood over the sword and kicked it further away.

"It looks like your time is up, Cuchulain!" Iroquois barked and he struck again, crashing heavily into his shield. The shield cracked and Iroquois hit it yet again.

It split, leaving Cuchulain unprotected and defeated.

Iroquois lifted his sword ready to finish Cuchulain who gazed up accepting his fate.

"Stop!" Lorna shouted reaching out to grab Graham's arm.

It was too late; Graham was running quickly across the cavern floor.

Iroquois stalled for a few seconds, not sure whether to finish Cuchulain. However, he found himself motionless, watching Graham slide across the floor reaching for Cuchulain's sword. Iroquois quickly came to his senses and turned quickly, advancing towards him. Graham grasped it in his hand and threw it towards Cuchulain.

Lorna screamed as Cuchulain reached out and grabbed the incoming sword out of the air.

Graham froze, helplessly lying on his back he gawped at the advancing Iroquois lifting his sword ready for the kill.

Chapter 18

The Mist Descends

PARALYSED, GRAHAM BRACED HIMSELF AND WATCHED AS the sword launched towards him. Taking a deep breath and closing his eyes, his final thoughts returned to his Uncle and how he had let him down. Just as he expected the contact, Lepy dived on top of him with a shield he grabbed off the floor, which shuddered and deafened them both as the sword struck, sending the shield spinning away across the floor. He was still alive, at least for a few seconds more.

As Iroquois purposely lifted his sword to complete the grisly act, a softly spoken voice whispered in the air, stopping him immediately in his tracks,

"Iroquois."

Iroquois paused and sensing Cuchulain was behind, quickly spun around, reaching out with his sword cunningly. To his terror the sword did not make contact. As the momentum carried him round, he noticed Cuchulain knelt down and his despairing swipe harmlessly passed over his head.

Iroquois' eyes filled with fear as he realised what was happening. Before he had time to bring his sword down again, Cuchulain thrust his sword with all his might through his rival's soft underbelly. Cuchulain twisted the magical sword, it glowed around the edge cutting through his flesh like butter and Iroquois let out a huge gasp, falling to his knees. His body fell on the stone floor face downwards and started to shudder; a dark shadow rose out of his body and drifted down disappearing into the stone earth. As it vanished, his body was still, Iroquois was dead.

Silence befell the cavern, Lorna and Graham glanced across at each other.

"Graham, this is not what I expected coming on holiday with you," Lorna said, sensing they were safe and quickly running up and giving him a hug.

Graham, a little embarrassed, started laughing, quickly joined by Lorna and Lepy, as the nervous tension released itself through laughter.

Graham glanced across noticing Carragah lying on his back on the floor.

"Are you OK Carragah?" he asked, kneeling down by his side.

He managed a slight smile. "Told you, Graham I am too old for this, Lepy, come help me to the lake."

Lepy climbed off the floor and moved towards Carragah. Cuchulain took control and went to Carragah.

With his strong physique he effortlessly assisted Carragah to his feet and silently moved towards the steps. As his foot touched the first step, the cavern shook and the entrance reopened.

"Come on Lorna and Graham, it's time to take you home," Lepy said, following Cuchulain and Carragah up the steps.

They all moved up the passages towards the exit. Graham noticed something on the floor and picked it up.

It was a silver chain with a green stone in it. Looking at the stone, he noticed white clouds swirling inside. He lifted it up towards the rays of sun which had started to penetrate this part of the passage. The clouds slowly vanished,

"Wow, is that an emerald?" Lorna gasped.

Graham shook his head and relooked at it. There were no clouds and it did resemble an emerald. Graham thought about quickly placing it in his pocket and keeping it but then thought better of it.

Carragah turned and slowly moved towards Graham as Cuchulain watched over him.

Reaching out he grabbed Graham's hand and he opened it, revealing the stone and chain. Carragah closed his fingers and smiled. "I think they have made a wise choice."

Graham looked up. "I don't understand?"

"You have been chosen to protect the secret burial grounds, this is a great honour."

"I can't, I'm just a boy."

"Graham, you have proven yourself today, you are brave and honest. You put your life on the line to protect this place, they have chosen well."

Carragah returned to Cuchulain and they went out to the dazzling sunshine.

Calm and tranquillity had returned to the countryside as the natural harmony buzzed infectiously.

Friesians were drifting aimlessly, chewing the endless supply of meadow as swallows chattered as they flew past like kamikaze pilots feasting on the abundant flies. The stone circle stood tall and proud, thankful that it too had played its part protecting the secret.

They arrived at the edge of the lake, Cuchulain linked Carragah and they placed their feet into the lightly surging water.

The air turned silent, only the sound of the water breaking against the rocks broke the atmosphere.

Gradually the lightly heaving water around their feet retracted in towards the centre of the lake as the small waves appeared to reverse their natural rhythm and fall backwards, carving open the lake until it revealed a concealed pathway. Thousands of heavy stones painstakingly laid reached into the hidden depths of the lake.

Graham and Lorna gazed out towards the centre of the lake observing the unparalleled force of nature's true power as it performed this amazing feat.

Carragah looked across at his three accomplices staring intently into the far reaches of the deepest lake and he beckoned them over towards where he stood.

"Lorna, I hope you enjoy the rest of your holiday. I am pleased to have met you and owe you a deep sense of gratitude. Without your help the secret burial grounds would surely have been lost!" Lorna smiled, her pretty face lighting up proudly.

"Lepy, my faithful servant, look out for these two, I fear they will require your assistance some time in the future. Your stature disguises your strong heart. I am forever in your debt and we will meet again! "

Carragah looked across at Graham and placed his hand on his shoulder, his wide blue eyes sparkling.

"Spud, when you look out over the rocky fields of Knocknakil, remember this sacred land has stood here for generations. The Burial Grounds must remain secret; they have made a wise choice placing them in your trust to watch just like your Uncle did previously. Be aware, just because Iroquois is dead does not mean the danger has passed. There are others. Lepy will be there to assist whenever you need. "

Carragah gazed at the three of them for a few seconds; he smiled and turned, Cuchulain nodded his head and they both stepped forwards.

After several steps on the secretive cobblestones, Cuchulain and Carragah turned one last time and smiled. They gazed at their friends; their faces were radiant, full of life and energy. Slowly they turned and walked until they had vanished into the mysterious lake, the sides of the corridor fell and the ripples returned. The sun's rays hit the water and it sparkled gleefully, the pulse of the waves returned, thriving and alive as if celebrating the long lost return of two extraordinary warriors.

Graham and Lorna watched, a small tear trickled down Graham's cheek as Lorna's eyes watered. They gazed longingly at the lake as several rainbow trout joined the celebration by somersaulting high out of the water and they wondered why it had to end this way.

The blue skies broke through as the sun's rays started to shine on this lush green countryside. Then a single white feather fell from the sky, just missing Graham's nose, and landed directly in front of him. He bent down and picked it up.

Slowly he turned to Lorna and said: "I think this is for you."

"A feather, what do I need a feather for?" She paused for a few seconds, thinking about it.

"Ah, I get it!" she exclaimed, as her face lit up realising its significance, and she excitedly linked him again.

"See you soon and next time I see you make sure you have your pot of gold with you!" Lepy said, a wry smile on his face.

"What's that over there?" he shouted pointing out towards the lake.

Graham and Lorna quickly looked over the lake but there was nothing out of the ordinary happening.

136

When they looked back, Lepy had vanished.

"I can't believe we fell for that," Lorna said, shaking her head.

"What a day, I'm glad it's over but..."

"Sad it's over!" Lorna interrupted.

"Yes, Carragah and Lepy really grew on me."

"Yeah, me too, we should head back though!"

"Yeah, you're right, come on then," Graham replied as they walked away from the Secret Burial Grounds, glancing back as they edged away.

In the dark forgotten valley near the ocean, the Boggot watched the events unfold through the flickering fire. He let out a long scream which expanded throughout the whole of Ireland and a large part of the ocean. All the cattle stopped chewing and the sheep huddled together, the swallows stopped chattering and all the birds took to the air. His blood red eyes peered out of the dark shadows...